A Collector's Guide to Magazine Paper Dolls

By
Mary Young

COLLECTOR BOOKS
A Division of Schroeder Publishing

Other Books By The Author

Paper Dolls and Their Artists - Book I
Paper Dolls and Their Artists - Book II
A Collector's Guide to Paper Dolls - Saalfield, Lowe and Merrill
A Collector's Guide to Paper Dolls - Second Series

The current values in this book should be used only as a guide. They are not intended to set prices, which vary from one section of the country to another. Auction prices as well as dealer prices vary greatly and are affected by condition as well as demand. Neither the Author nor the Publisher assumes responsibility for any losses that might be incurred as a result of consulting this guide.

Dedication

To seven little ones, very dear to my heart –
Maria, Benjamin, Phillip, Becky, Patrick, Mary Sarah
and Gretchen.

Acknowledgments

I want to thank the following people who have helped me with this book:

First to my husband, George, for all his help and encouragement I want to especially express my gratitude.

To Betsy Addison, Lila Allen, Norene Allen, Fay Jean Anderson, Marianne Anderson, Marlene Brenner, Donna Brinkman, Carol Carey, Pat Dahlberg, Rosemary Davidson, Helen Dixon, Ilene Duluk, Shirley Edgerley, Peggy Ell, Jenny Elmore, Rosalie Eppert, Barbara Faber, Patti Fertel, Robin Goldstein, Jean Hart, Shirley Hedge, Donna Heiser, Judy Herta, Pam Hunter, Helen Johnson, Judy Johnson, Elaine Kantor, Mary Kelley, Carol Kennedy, Neelie Lang, Judy Lawson, Judy Le Jeune, Louise Leek, Joan McCraw, Gladys Merrell, Cynthia Musser, Jean Rash, Winifred Sillery, Betsy Slap, Madeline Smith, Jean Sullivan, Emma Terry, Edna Turnipseed, Fran Van Vynckt, Emy Varsolona, Janie Varsolona, Edith White, Ann Wilmer, Virginia Wolz and Wynn Yusas; their willingness to check their lists, send material for photographing and help in any way they could is greatly appreciated.

A very special thanks to Virginia Crossley for her lengthy assistance and furnishing a large percentage of the paper doll material used in this book.

My appreciation also goes to Teresa Canuti, James Mann and Margaret Peiffer for their assistance.

A special tribute to the memory of Louise Kaufman and Jane Sugg who found such great pleasure in collecting the magazine paper dolls.

I also want to thank all of you who have waited so patiently for this book to be completed. I am deeply grateful for your unwavering support.

Note: *The paper dolls are from the author's collection unless otherwise noted. All photographs are by the author unless otherwise noted.*

Paper dolls pictured are in mint condition and are priced as such. Some photos are cropped for production purposes.

Introduction

"Dolly Dingle," "Lettie Lane," "Betty Bonnet"; one or all of these names brings a smile of recollection to the faces of so many who have been fascinated by these paper dolls since the first quarter of this century. These paper dolls and many more may never have come to reality had it not been for those lovely magazines devoted to the women of the family. Store-bought paper dolls were not as common in those early years, but most women's magazines had a page for children, and many of these pages included paper dolls from time to time. Some paper dolls appeared in American magazines during the 19th century as well, and the honor of having the first paper dolls most likely goes to the *Godey's Lady's Book* which had paper dolls as far back as 1859.

Often a cut-out paper toy or a page with stand-up figures would be featured instead of a paper doll. In most cases, these pages have not been shown here because of space limitations. However, when possible, one example of a highly collectible paper toy series has been shown. When a very popular paper doll series has related pages they have been pictured also; for example, "Dolly Dingle's Christmas Cards" in the "Dolly Dingle" series.

For those of you who have not yet experienced the fascination of collecting magazine paper dolls, I hope this book will bring about a new awareness of these delightful paper dolls and that you will derive pleasure from seeing them possibly for the first time.

This is an example of a paper toy page which has a building to put together and stand-up figures. This page was in the "Tiny In Tinytown" series and appeared in the October 1915 issue of *The Delineator*.

Contents

The American Woman – "Playmates From Storyland"

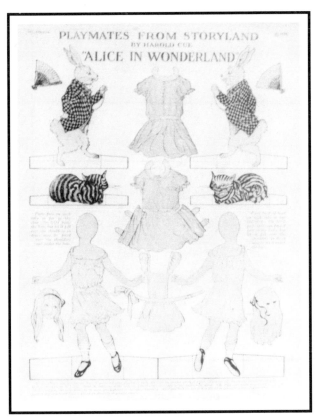

September 1921
"Alice In Wonderland"

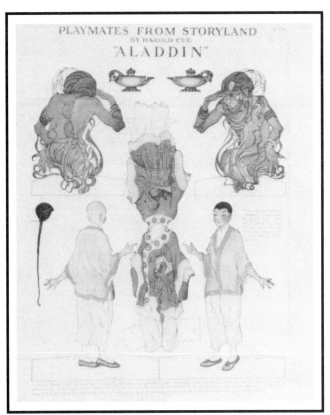

December 1921
"Aladdin"

November 1921
"Pandora"

October 1921
"Robinson Crusoe"

This series of 12 pages was done in iimited color with shades of orange, brown, red or grey.
All "Playmates From Storyland" pages are from the collection of Virginia Crossley.

January 1922
"Heidi"

February 1922
"King Arthur"

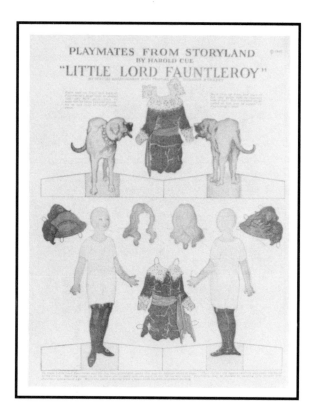

March 1922
"Little Lord Fauntleroy"

April 1922
"Jo" from "Little Women"

May 1922
"Hiawatha"

July 1922
"The Princess and the Goblin"

August 1922
"Hans Brinker"

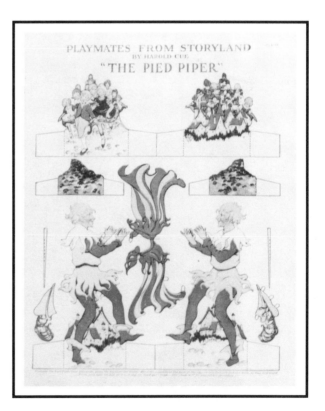

September 1922
"The Pied Piper"

Author's Note: The existence of a June 1922 issue is unknown.

American Family Journal

The first issue of *American Family Journal* was in November 1904 and was published in New York.

November 1910
"Mother Goose Family"
Courtesy of Winifred Sillery

Butterick Fashion Magazine

The Summer Number 1935
"Barbara Jane"
Courtesy of Carol Carey

Canadian Home Journal

November 1933 Cover

The *Canadian Home Journal* was published by the Consolidated Press Limited in Toronto, Canada. It began in 1904 and ran to 1958. Research was done on issues dating from July 1928 to April 1939. The years from July 1928 to December 1931 could not be researched completely as some copies either were not available or had pages missing. However, the information found from the January 1932 to April 1939 issues is complete.

All of the paper doll pages are in limited color (black, white and one additional color such as red, orange or blue).

If a date does not appear between January 1932 and April 1939, then there was no paper doll in that particular issue.

The following paper dolls are known to exist but pictures were not available.

July 1928 – "Comfy the Toy Poodle"
August 1928 – "Mollie Cottontail"
October 1928 – "Kathleen and Her Kitty"

**November 1928
"Mary Louise and Pussykins"
Courtesy of Robin Goldstein**

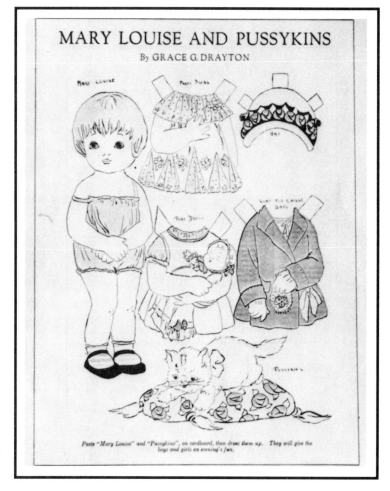

December 1928
"The Christmas Skating Girl"
Courtesy of Robin Goldstein

February 1929
"The Skating Partner"
From the Louise Kaufman Collection

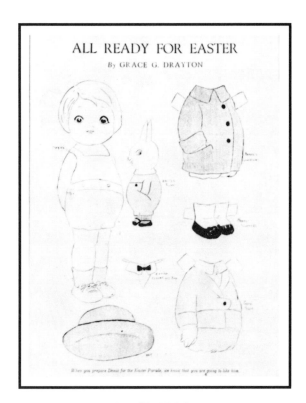

April 1929
"All Ready For Easter"

October 1929
"Who Doesn't Love a Teddy Bear?"

March 1929 "Just a School Day Reminder" was not available to photograph.

**November 1929
"Maudie and More of
Her Playmates"**

**December 1929
"Tillie's Dream of Christmas"**

The October 1930 issue contains a story "Ann Marie and the Paper Dolls," but actual paper dolls are not included.

**March 1932
"Mary Lou's Baby Sister Sally"**

February 1932 "Joan and Bobby Go To a Valentine Party" was not available for photograph.

April 1932
"Mary Lou's Spring Clothes"

May 1932
"Mary Lou's Chum Babs"

June 1932
"Ann's Holiday Clothes"

July 1932
"Bobby Goes to Banff"

August 1932
"Joan's New Clothes"

September 1932
"Mandy"

October 1932
"Topsy"

November 1932
"Babs and Billy"

December 1932
"Mary Lou and Santa Claus"

January 1933
"Sue Goes South"

February 1933
"Mary Lou and Bobby
Go To Dancing School"

March 1933
"Mary Lou's Mother"

April 1933
"Joan and Billy's Easter Party"

May 1933
"Mary Lou's Father"

June 1933
"Bab's Holiday Clothes"

July 1933
"Topsy's Brother Sam"

August 1933
"Mary Lou's Cousin June"

September 1933
"Mary Lou Goes To School"

November 1933
"Mary Lou's Cousin Ann"

March 1934
"Topsy"

April 1934
"Mary Lou and Bobby At Easter"

May 1934
"Bab's Spring Clothes"

October 1934
"Joan and Bobby
Go To A Halloween Party"

November 1934
"Mary Lou's Cousin Joan"

September 1934 "Mary Lou's Mother" was not available to photograph.

**December 1935
"Mary Lou and Joan
Christmas Day"**

**January 1936
"June and Billy"**

**February 1936
"Mary Lou"**

**March 1936
"Sue and Joan"**

May 1936
"Babs and Billy"

June 1936
"Mary Lou and Billy"

December 1936
"Mary Lou and Bobby's Christmas"

Close-up of the Shirley Temple paper doll that appeared on the December 1936 paper doll page.

April 1937
"June's Spring Clothes"

May 1937
"Ann"

June 1937
**"Sue and Babs Attend a
June Wedding"**

January 1938
"Mary Lou's Father"

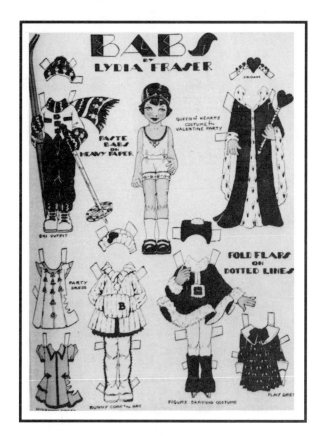

February 1938
"Babs"

March 1938
"Joan and Billy"

April 1938
**"June and Mary Lou's
Easter Clothes"**

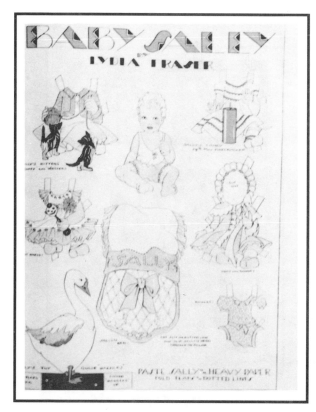

May 1938
"Baby Sally"

June 1938 "Ann"　　　　**September 1938 "Babs Goes to School"**

Children's Vogue

Children's Vogue was published in New York from 1919 to 1925. In 1925, the magazine united with *Vogue Pattern Book.* The magazine was known as *Children's Costume Royal* at the beginning with a change to *Children's Royal* and then *Children's Vogue.*

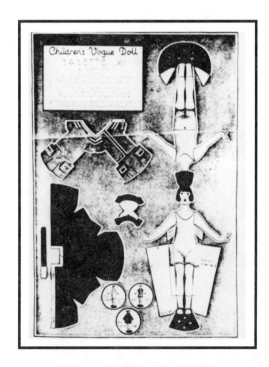

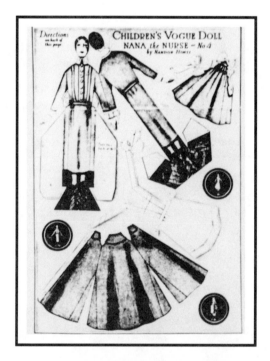

February/March 1924　　　　**August/September 1924**
"Children's Vogue Doll –　　　**"Children's Vogue Doll – Nana**
Babette No. 1"　　　　　　**The Nurse No. 4"**
Courtesy of Marlene Brenner　**Courtesy of Marlene Brenner**

Photographs not available for No. 2 or for No. 3 (Nancy).

Comfort

Comfort magazine was published in Augusta, Maine by the W. H. Gannett Publishers, Inc. from 1888 to 1942. The earliest known paper doll page appeared in December 1895. Then the next known paper dolls began in October 1913. Magazines were checked from December 1912 through September 1921 with some issues missing. All of the paper dolls found are pictured here. The magazines, at least in the time period covered here, were printed on paper similar to a newspaper, so over the years the magazines have become brittle and yellowed. The only color used was on the covers of the magazine so all paper dolls were in black and white with the possible exception of the paper dolls that appeared on two covers in 1914.

December 1910 cover of *Comfort* magazine

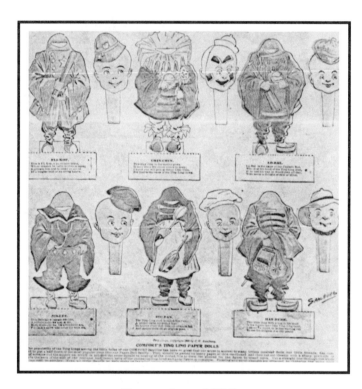

**December 1895
"Comfort's Ting Ling Paper Dolls"
Courtesy of Ann Wilmer**

Other pages of paper dolls may have been appearing in *Comfort* this same year as these paper dolls were "to help make up the great paper doll family being published by *Comfort*." It is known that the March 1896 issue had "Comical Marionette Ting Lings."

**October 1913
"Dolly Prim and Her Dresses"
Courtesy of Joan McCraw**

November 1913
**"Dolly Prim's
Thanksgiving"
Courtesy of
Helen Johnson"**

The March 1914 page is "Dolly Prim's Cupboard and Dishes." There are dishes and a stand-up cupboard to cut out but no paper dolls.

December 1913
**"Dolly Prim and
Her Christmas Tree"
Courtesy of Rosalie Eppert**

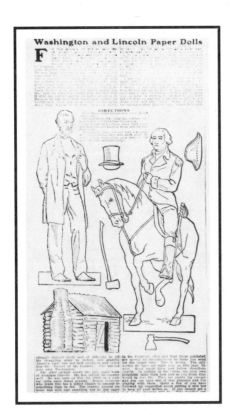

February 1914
**"Washington and
Lincoln Paper Dolls"
Courtesy of
Helen Johnson**

Two paper dolls appeared on covers of *Comfort* in 1914. The dolls were with a front and back to be pasted together. There were no extra outfits for the dolls. A story was on the inside of the magazine. January 1914 was "Dolly Prim In Winter Clothes" and May 1914 was "Dolly Prim and Little Bo-Peep."

April 1914
**"Story About Dolly
Prim/Dolly Prim
and Her Dresses"**

**January 1915
"Dress Up Teddy Bear"**

**March 1915
"Bunny Rabbit Dolly"
Courtesy of
Rosalie Eppert**

**May 1915
"Dolly Prim and Her Dresses"**

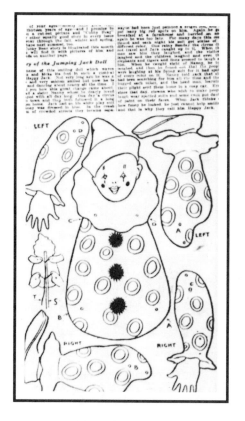

**September 1915
"Story of the Jumping
Jack Doll"
("Children's Happy Hour"
appeared at top of page.)**

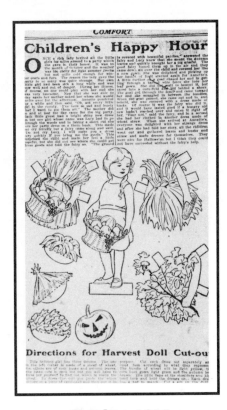

October 1915
"Children's Happy Hour"
("Harvest Doll")

November 1915
"Children's Happy Hour"
("Thanksgiving Doll")
Courtesy of Gladys Merrell

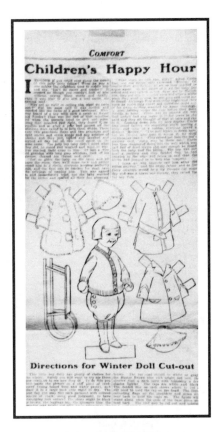

December 1915
"Children's Happy Hour"
("Winter Doll")
Courtesy of Gladys Merrell

January 1916
"Children's Happy Hour"
(Doll's name in story is
"Snowdrop.")

February 1916
"Children's Happy Hour"
("Dolly Dewdrop")

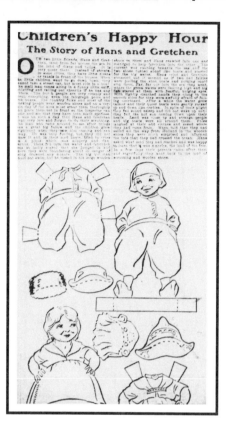

March 1916
"Children's Happy Hour The Story of Hans and Gretchen"

April 1916
"April Boy Doll"
("Children's Happy Hour" appeared at top of page.)

May 1916
"Children's Happy Hour Story of Little Queen of May"
Courtesy of Pam Hunter

November 1916
"Children's Happy Hour
Violet's Magic Curls"

December 1916
"Children's Happy Hour
– Matilda's Happy
Christmas"

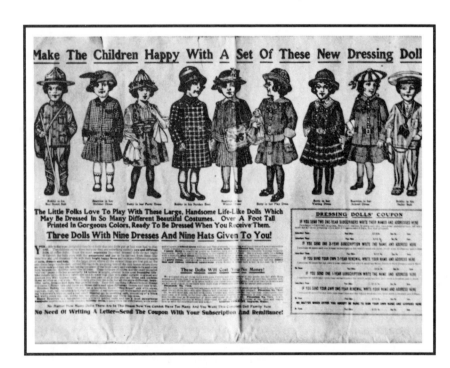

December 1916
"Make the Children Happy With A Set of These New
Dressing Dolls!" An advertisement showing paper
dolls given away free for subscriptions to *Comfort*.
(Similar ads appeared in October and November of
1916 with these same paper dolls.)

January 1917
"Martha's Kitten"
("Children's Happy
Hour" appeared at the
top of the page.)
Courtesy of
Joan McCraw

**February 1917
"Dorothy's Forest Friends"
("Children's Happy Hour"
appeared at top of page.)**

**March 1917
"Children's Happy Hour
Matilda and the Frog"**

The April 1917 page is "Children's Happy Hour – Chub, The Pet Pony." The page includes a pony, cart and two children that fit in the cart (not pictured).

**February 1918
"The Uncle Sam Doll" ("Children's
Happy Hour" appeared at the top
of the page.)
Courtesy of Helen Johnson**

**November 1919
"Little Dorothy The Cut-Out
Doll – Dorothy At The Sea-
shore" (date not verified)
Courtesy of Rosalie Eppert**

The Delineator

The Delineator was published by The Butterick Publishing Company in New York. The first issue was in 1873. The first Butterick pattern was issued 10 years earlier. *The Delineator* merged with *The Designer* and *The Woman's Magazine* in 1926. (The latter two magazines had united in 1920). In 1937, *The Delineator* merged with *Pictorial Review* but then two years later, in 1939, publication ceased. (From 1926 until 1937 the title was *Delineator*.)

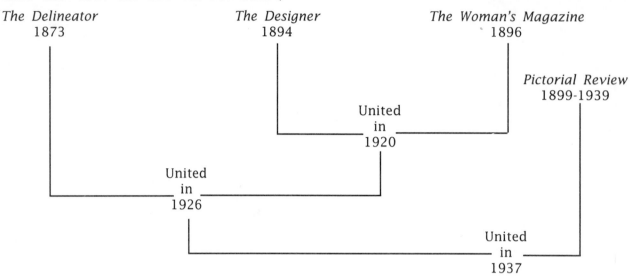

The following is a list of the cut-out children's pages which appeared in *The Delineator* after 1910. If a date is not given, no cut-out page appeared in that issue. The paper doll pages are pictured following the list.

"Scissors Pictures" began in September 1910 and appeared periodically through May 1912. These were cut-out pictures and did not contain paper dolls or stand-up paper figures.

1912
Carolyn Chester's Full-Base Paper Dolls
February - "Adele" (first of the series)
March - "Adele" (party dress)
April - "Adele" (Easter suit)
June - "Adele's Little Sister"
July - "When Adele's Little Sister Goes To Bed"
August - "Adele's Little Sister: You Named Her Betty, Children."
September - "Your Own Toy Aeroplane, Children"
October - "Giving Dolly A Halloween Party"
November - "Mammy Cook and Her Thanksgiving Dinner"
December - "Keeping Christmas With Susan and the Mermaids" (two pages)

August 1919 cover of *The Delineator*

1913
Carolyn Chester's Round-Base Paper Dolls Given Historic Value
January - "Watch Us Celebrate Our 50th Birthday. The First Butterick Pattern Was Cut At Sterling, Mass. in 1863." (two pages)
February - No paper dolls or stand-ups; however, this issue includes "How to make Mr. Butterick's Little Home Village, Sterling," with directions for making three miniature buildings. A full-page painting "Fifty Years Ago in Sterling," also appears in this issue.
March - "The Sterling Twins"
April - "These Dolls Are Dressed As Pretty French Ladies Were When Butterick Fashions First Went To Paris."
May - "These Dolls Show The Prevailing Fashions of 1903"
June - "From Sterling Fifty Years Ago To Paris Today – The World Journey of the Butterick Pattern."
Each of the above issues except June has a beautiful full-page portrait of a "Delineator Girl." The sixth and last portrait appeared in July (below).

Margaret Butterick Series
July - "Margaret Butterick, The Cut-Out Doll That Opens and Shuts Her Eyes"
September - "Margaret's Little Brother, Bobby Butterick, Children"
October - "Margaret Butterick's Little Sister Betty and Her Doll, Bettina"
November - "Your Butterick Dolls Go To Grandmother's For Thanksgiving" (a cut-out page of a bedroom with bed for the Butterick paper dolls)

1914
January - "Hang Up Baby Butterick's Stocking"
February - "When Your Butterick Paper Dolls Have Dinner" (a cut-out page with a table that the paper dolls can sit at and food to place on the table.)

Peter Newell's Movies began in May 1914 and ran through October 1914. They appeared again in January and April 1915 when the series ended. These were children's cut-outs but did not contain paper dolls or stand-up figures.

1915
Our New Cut-Out: Tiny In Tinytown (stand-up buildings and figures)
May - A cottage, Tiny and other townspeople
June - The town hall, candy shop, townspeople and automobile
July - The fire station, firemen, horses and fire engines

August - The school, teacher (Miss Spectacles), children, grocery store and grocer
September - The church, Sunday school teacher, infant class, minister, other townspeople and the grocer's delivery horse and wagon
October - The Globe Department Store, store employees, delivery automobile

1916 - No paper dolls or paper toys

1917
Who Are They? Patten Beard Presents Peter Pan's Movie Contest
March - "Who Are They?" Number One
April - "Who Are They?" Number Two (on the back of this page are Easter Greeting cards titled, "Easter Greetings For Girls and Boys.")
May - "Who Are They?" Number Three
June - "Who Are They?" Number Four
July - "Who Are They?" Number Five
August - "Who Are They?" Number Six

A series of World War I cut-out pages appeared periodically in 1917 and 1918. Some did contain paper dolls so the complete series is pictured.
September - "A Model Battleship From Captain Jack To Billy Mascot."
October - No World War I page in this issue but there is a children's page of place cards to cut out titled, "A Halloween Carnival."
November - "A Naval Airplane With Its Daring Crew"
December - No World War I page in this issue but there are two pages (back to back) of Christmas cards.

1918
January - "With An Ambulance On The Firing-Line."
March - "On Furlough In France"
May - "Tommy Atkins on Furlough"
June - "On Leave At His Home in Sunny Italy."

The Delineator Children's Theater (with stand-up figures)
July - "Snow White"
August - "Cinderella, In Two Acts"
September - "Jack and the Beanstalk"
October - "The Wild Swans"
December - "Whittington, A Play"

1919
January - "Alice in Wonderland"
February - "A Valentine Romance"
March - "This Way For the Big Circus" (a circus card game, not part of theater series)
April - "Robinson Crusoe, in Two Acts"

May - "Launcelot and Elaine"

June - "The Pied Piper of Hamelin"

This was the end of "The Delineator Children's Theater" series.

July - "Soldiers of Three Wars and Their Lasses"

August - "The Nursery Playhouse - I - The Little Red Hen" (stand-up figures)

September - "The Nursery Playhouse - II - Chicken Licken" (stand-up figures)

October - "Help The Delineator Rebuild This Town" (cut and paste picture)

November - "The Nursery Playhouse - III - The Old Woman and Her Pig" (stand-up figures)

December - "Santa's Transatlantic Flight" (cut and paste picture)

1920

January - "The Nursery Playhouse IV - Three Little Pigs and The Wolf" (stand-up figures)

February - "Story of the Five Little Pigs" (story pictures)

March - "Little Miss Muffet" (story pictures)

April - "Hey Diddle Diddle" (story pictures)

July/August - "Let's Give Them A Ford!" (cut and paste picture)

1921

January - "The Slippery Faces" (cut and paste picture)

February - "Dell Is The Doll With The Newest Dresses"

April - "Dell Is A Very Lucky Little Paper Doll ..."

August - "Daisy Gives A Garden Party"

December - "Christmas Day In Holland" (Betty Butterick stand-up figures)

1922

January - "Betty Butterick Goes To Spain" (stand-up figures)

February - "The Little Delineator," (a page for children began this month; no Betty Butterick page this issue.)

March - "Betty Butterick In England" (stand-up figures)

April - "Betty Butterick In France" (stand-up figures)

May - "Betty Goes To Norway and Sweden" (stand-up figures)

June - "Betty's Visit To The Italian Children" (stand-up figures)

July - "Betty In The Swiss Alps" (stand-up figures)

"The Little Delineator," a page started in February 1922, ran until February 1927. The children could fold the page to form a little magazine of their own. It contained stories, things to do, contests, letters and poems, but no paper dolls were featured.

February 1912
Courtesy of Virginia Crossley

March 1912

April 1912
Courtesy of Virginia Crossley

June 1912

July 1912
Courtesy of Virginia Crossley

August 1912
Courtesy of Virginia Crossley

September 1912
Courtesy of Virginia Crossley

October 1912
Courtesy of Virginia Crossley

November 1912
Courtesy of Helen Johnson

December 1912

January 1913
(The first page of two.)
Courtesy of Virginia Crossley

January 1913
(The second page of two.)
Courtesy of Virginia Crossley

March 1913
Courtesy of Virginia Crossley

April 1913
Courtesy of Virginia Crossley

May 1913

June 1913
Courtesy of Virginia Crossley

MARGARET BUTTERICK THE CUT-OUT DOLL THAT OPENS AND SHUTS HER EYES

**July 1913
Courtesy of Virginia Crossley**

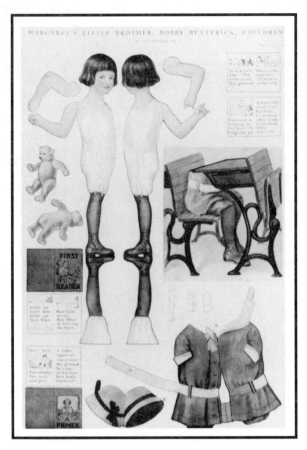

September 1913
Courtesy of Virginia Crossley

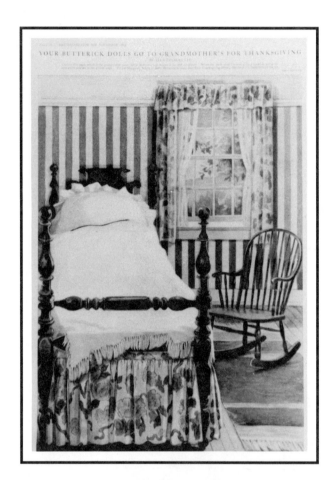

November 1913
Courtesy of Virginia Crossley

October 1913
Courtesy of Virginia Crossley

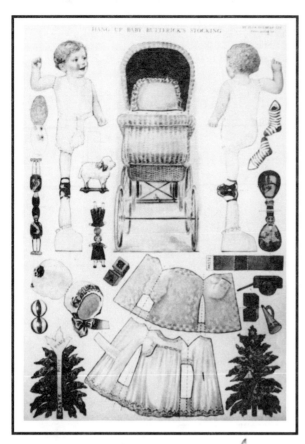

January 1914

February 1914

March 1917
Courtesy of Virginia Crossley

April 1917
Courtesy of Virginia Crossley

May 1917
Courtesy of Virginia Crossley

June 1917
Courtesy of Virginia Crossley

July 1917
Courtesy of Virginia Crossley

August 1917

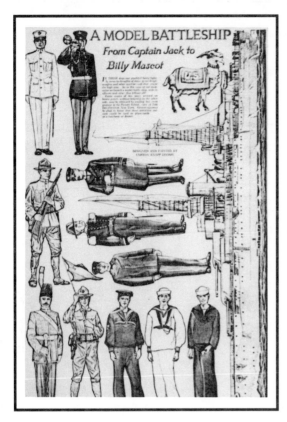

September 1917

November 1917

January 1918

March 1918
Courtesy of Donna Heiser

May 1918

June 1918

June 1919
This is an example of one sheet from "The Delineator Children's Theater" series. The theater includes stand-up figures but not paper dolls.

SOLDIERS OF THREE WARS AND THEIR LASSES

Here is Sam, home from war. And you, all ready for him, "dolled up" in your prettiest pretties, just as grandmother was before you in Civil War times, and great-grandmother after the Revolution, when their boys came home.

Before cutting out the figures and the clothes, look for all the places to be slit, and cut them carefully with a knife. To make the figures stand, fold C forward, E backward, and D under; paste the point of D under C.

All the tabs marked BF should be bent backward and pasted together at the tips. Tabs B bend backward, they just hook over head, shoulder, etc. Tabs marked A slip into slits without bending.

July 1919

February 1921
Courtesy of Virginia Crossley

April 1921

August 1921

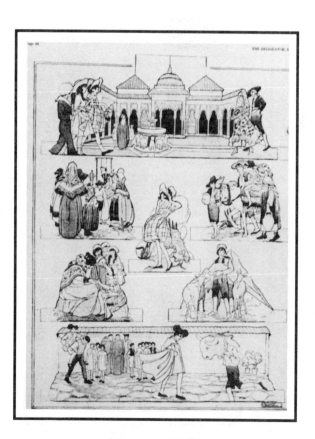

January 1922
This is an example of one sheet from the "Betty Butterick" series. The page includes stand-up figures but not paper dolls.

The Designer

The Designer was originally called *Standard Delineator* when it began publication in 1894. Perhaps some confusion was caused with this name owing to the fact that another magazine, the popular *Delineator,* had already been in publication for more than 20 years. For whatever the reason, in 1896 the magazine became known as *Standard Designer.* The name *Standard* was dropped in 1898, and the magazine became *The Designer.* In April 1920, *The Designer* united with *The Woman's Magazine,* and the magazine became known as *The Designer and The Woman's Magazine.* The magazine was eventually absorbed by *Delineator* in 1926 which in turn merged with *Pictorial Review* in 1937. The end came in 1939 when *Pictorial Review* ceased publication.

A series of children's pages appeared in late 1917 and early 1918 which included some paper dolls. These delightful pages were done by the artist, Bell Colborne, and are pictured here. One series that did not include paper dolls was "The Fairy Playhouse" which appeared intermittently from September 1912 until May 1914 and contained stand-up figures. Another was a cut-out page called "Pictoweaves" that started in November 1911 and appeared off and on until March 1913. The pages contained strips of paper to cut out and weave to form a picture. Two pages which were meant for the woman of the house most likely ended up in the hands of the children. They were "A Living Room for the Woman Who Dares" (August 1919), and "A Room All Black and Blue" (January 1920). Each page pictures a room which is void of any furniture. At the bottom of the page are different pieces of furniture that could be cut out and pasted in the room. A cute page in the December 1917 issue titled, "Old Friends In New Shapes," showed separate wooden toys that very likely were cut out by the children. A three-part story/poem called "The Paper Doll Family" started in September 1914 but, alas, did not include actual paper dolls to cut out.

**October 1917
"Sylvia and Her Seven Frocks"**

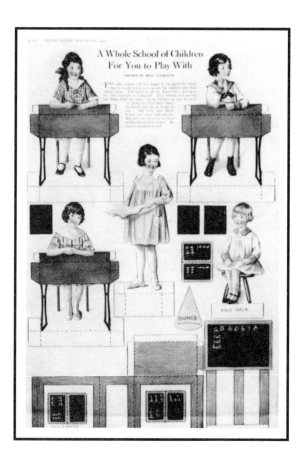

November 1917
"A Whole School of Children
For You To Play With"

**November 1917
"A Whole School of Children
For You To Play With"**

**March 1918
"Sylvia Does Her Marketing"**

**January 1918
"When The Doctor Comes"**

The Dolls' Dressmaker – A Magazine For Girls

In January 1891, Volume One, Number One of *The Dolls' Dressmaker* made its appearance. The editor was Jennie Wren, and the magazine sold for 50¢ a year (later raised to $1.00 in 1892). The magazine was devoted to little girls and their handiwork. The editor felt that little girls could acquire a love for sewing if they could sew clothes for their dolls while they were young. And beginning with the first issue, a full page of styles for dolls' outfits was shown in the form of paper dolls. The first issue had a lady doll with two front-and-back outfits.

Articles, stories, poems, game instructions, full-page paintings, patterns for outfits and letters were also included in this publication which apparently lasted only three years. The last known issue is December 1893, and all research indicates that it was no longer published after that date even though the December 1893 issue includes a form to fill out for a year's subscription.

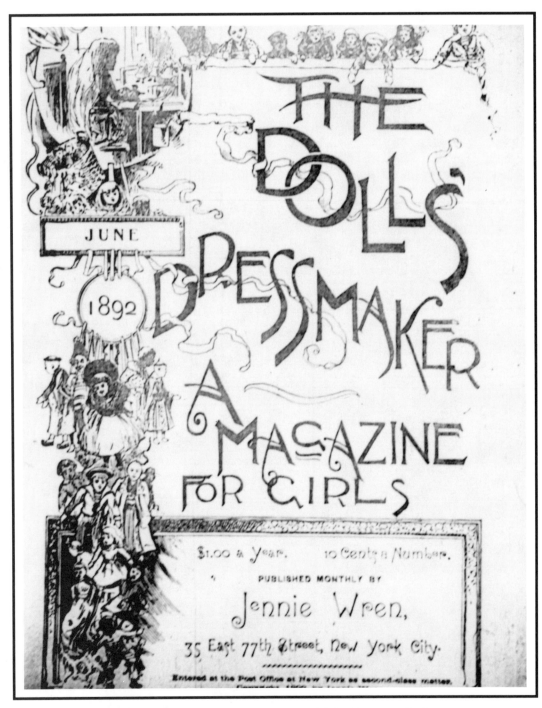

June 1892 cover of *The Dolls' Dressmaker*

January 1891
"Walking Dress and Ball Costume
For Lady Doll"

February 1891
"Doll's Fashions"

March 1891
"Boy and Girl Doll Costumes"

April 1891
"Dollie In The Kitchen"
Courtesy of Rosalie Eppert

May 1891
"Doll Costumes and Furniture"
Courtesy of Rosalie Eppert

June 1891 (date not verified)
"Seaside Styles For Dollie"
Courtesy of Rosalie Eppert

July 1891
"Seaside Styles for Dollie"
Courtesy of Rosalie Eppert

August 1891 (date not verified)
"Seasonable Styles For Dollie"
Courtesy of Rosalie Eppert

September 1891
"Styles For Baby Doll and Nurse Doll"

October 1891
"Dollie Housecleaning"

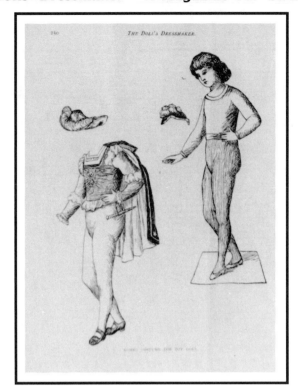

November 1891
"Romeo Costume For Boy Doll"
Courtesy of Rosalie Eppert

December 1891
"Front of Doll's Bridal Dress"

January 1892
"Back of Doll's Bridal Dress"
(Note: the back of the bridal
dress was drawn much larger
than the front of the dress which
appeared in the December 1891
issue.)

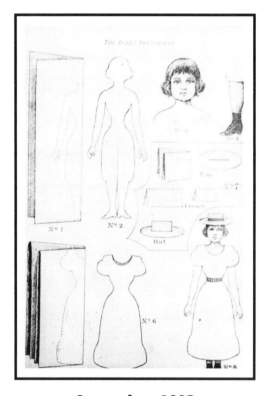

September 1893
"A Lesson In Doll Making"
No paper dolls could be found
after January 1892 until this
page in September 1893.
However, a few issues were
missing with the possibility
that at least one of them
contained a paper doll.

Extension Magazine

The *Extension Magazine* is published in Chicago by the Catholic Church Extension Society of the United States of America. Publication began in 1906 and continues to the present time. In 1940, the word "Magazine" was dropped from the title, and the periodical was known as *Extension* from then on.

A paper doll page was started in June 1931 and continued through June 1936 with just a few interruptions of puzzles or other types of cut-out pages. "Father Peter Cutouts" began in October 1943 and ran until January 1944. Another "Father Peter Cutouts" page appeared in June 1950 and one reprint from the series was shown in March 1954 and another in September 1959.

The paper doll pages were done in limited color using black, white and one other color such as green, red or brown, but sometimes two shades of the third color would be used.

A special thank you to Virginia Crossley for supplying the material for the following list and pictures.

1931
June - "Patsy"
July - "Patsy's Brother Tom"
August - "Patsy's Little Sister Diana"
September - "Patsy's Baby Sister"
October - "Patsy's Hallowe'en Party"
November - "Tom's Friend Jerry"
December - "Patsy's Christmas"

1932
January - "Patsy's Chum Joan"
February - "Patsy's Valentine Party"
March - "Patsy's Mother"
April - "Patsy's Dolls"
May - "Patsy's Birthday Party"
June - "Patsy's Vacation"
July - "Patsy's Sister Diana Goes To Camp"
August - "Patsy's Brother Tom Goes To The Seashore"
September - "Patsy Goes to Fairyland"
October - "Patsy Arrives in Patchwork Land"
November - "Patsy Visits The King and Queen of Patchwork Land" (stand-up figures)
December - "Home of the Patchwork Family" (stand-up house, trees, etc.)

1933
January - "Patsy Meets The Magic Horse"
February - "Patsy And The Good Pirates"
March - "Patsy Visits The People Of The Deep Sea City"
April - "Patsy Meets The Easter Bunny" (jigsaw puzzle)
May - "Ave Maria" (jigsaw puzzle)
June - "The Swing" (jigsaw puzzle)
July - "Independence Day" (jigsaw puzzle)
August - "At The Seashore" (jigsaw puzzle)
September - "Picking Apples" (jigsaw puzzle)
October - "Something New For The Kiddies" (picture parts to fit a scene)
November - "A Thanksgiving Day Picture" (picture parts to fit a scene)
December - "A Christmas Picture For Children" (picture parts to fit a scene)

1934
January - "The Snow Man" (picture parts to fit a scene)
February - "A Valentine Party" (picture parts to fit a scene)
March - "Our Little French Friends, Antoine and Antoinette"
April - "Our Swedish Friends, Chris and Christina"
May - "Once Upon a Time In Russia; Sonya and Sanine"
June - "Our Little Friends From Holland, Hans and Hermenia"
July - "Our Little Italian Friends, Mario and Maria"
August - "Our Little German Friends, Wilhelm and Wilhelmina"
September - "The Circus Parade" (picture parts to fit a scene)
October - "The Circus Parade" (picture parts to fit a scene)
November - "The Circus Parade" (picture parts to fit a scene)
December - "The Circus Parade" (picture parts to fit a scene)

1935
January - "The Circus Parade" (picture parts to fit a scene)
February - "The Circus Parade" (picture parts to fit a scene)
March - "Patsy Comes Back"
April - "Patsy's Twin Brother Pat"
May - "Patsy's Little Sister Joan"
June - "Patsy's Baby Brother Jackie"
July - "Patsy's Friend, Dotty"
August - "Patsy's Friend, Dickie"
September - "Mother Goose Cutouts" (stand-up figures)

October - "Another Mother Goose Tale" (stand-up figures)

November - "Old Mother Hubbard" (stand-up figures)

December - "Jack and Jill" (stand-up figures)

1936

January - "Little Bo-Peep" (stand-up figures)

February - "Rub-A-Dub-Dub" (stand-up figures)

March - "Molly"

April - "Molly's Brother, Jimmy"

May - "Molly's Friend, Greta"

June - "Molly's Little Brother Danny"

June 1931   July 1931

1943

October - "Father Peter and His Vestments"

November - "Father Peter Cutouts: The Altar" (stand-up piece)

December - "Father Peter Cutouts" (stand-up pieces for the altar)

1944

January - "Father Peter Cutouts" (stand-up pieces)

September - No cut-out page but the cover shows a little girl playing with the "Father Peter Cutouts."

1950

June - "Father Peter Cutouts; Presenting Paul, The Altar Boy"

1954

March - "Father Peter Cutouts; Presenting Paul, The Altar Boy" (exact reprint of June 1950)

1959

September - "Learn About The Mass" (A reprint of October 1943, with the same doll and outfits but arranged differently on the page with a different write-up.)

August 1931
September 1931

Patsy's Hallowe'en Party
By Martha E. Miller

Tom's Friend Jerry
By Martha E. Miller

October 1931

November 1931

December 1931
January 1932

April 1932   May 1932

February 1932
March 1932

June 1932   **July 1932**

August 1932   **September 1932**

October 1932   **November 1932**

December 1932   **January 1933**

February 1933   **March 1933**

March 1934   **April 1934**   **May 1934**   **June 1934**

OUR LITTLE ITALIAN FRIENDS
MARIO AND MARIA
designed by MARTHA E. MILLER

Maria's Hat

Mario

Maria's Tarantella Dress

Maria's Shawl

Mario's Cap

Mario's Tarantella Suit

Maria

OUR LITTLE GERMAN FRIENDS
WILHELM AND WILHELMINA
designed by MARTHA E. MILLER

Wilhelm's Costume

Wilhelmina's Hat

Cut on Dotted Line

Wilhelm's Hat

Wilhelm

Wilhelmina

Cut on Dotted Line

Wilhelmina's Head-dress

Wilhelmina's Costume

July 1934

August 1934

March 1935   **April 1935**   **May 1935**   **June 1935**

July 1935   **August 1935**

March 1936   **April 1936**   **May 1936**   **June 1936**

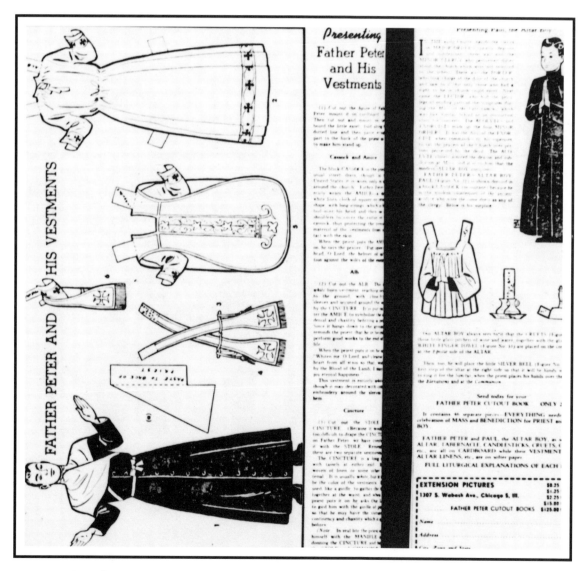

October 1943   **June 1950**

The October 1943 page was reprinted in September 1959 with the title, "Learn About the Mass." The June 1950 page was reprinted in March 1954.

The Farm Journal

The Farm Journal began in 1877 and is still published today. The following are the only known paper dolls published by the magazine.

November 1921
"A New Paper Doll"
Courtesy of Helen Johnson

November 1924
"A Page Of Cut-Out Cutey-Dolls"

October 1956
"Our Paper Polly Helps You Color-Cue Your Clothes"
Courtesy of Helen Johnson

The Farmer

In the year of 1882, Edward A. Webb of Fargo, North Dakota founded a publication called *The Northwestern Farmer*. In 1890, he moved the magazine to St. Paul, Minnesota and organized the Webb Publishing Co. "Northwestern" was dropped from the title in 1898, and the magazine became known as *The Farmer*. Through the years, The Webb Publishing Co. acquired other farming magazines and with the acquisition of *The Dakota Farmer* in 1980, the combined publications were reaching 200,000 farm families.

A paper doll series appeared on the "Our Children's Page" periodically from Jan. 8, 1927 to April 13, 1929. (*The Farmer* became a weekly in 1910.) The paper dolls were in black and white and were in a block which usually measured about 4½" x 6½". The first paper doll is of a little girl named Virginia who takes a trip around the world and sends back a paper doll of a child from each country she visits. Beginning with the 3rd paper doll, the series is called "Dolls of All Nations," and each doll is now numbered. The last paper doll (#24) is from Canada. Four of the paper dolls are shown following the list of all 24 paper dolls. Also pictured are the paper dolls that were published in more recent years.

The Farmer/The Dakota Farmer celebrated its 100th anniversary in 1982 and continues to publish a highly informative magazine for the farm families. It is now published semi-monthly except monthly in June, July and December.

"Dolls of All Nations" series (printed in black and white)

January 8, 1927 (#1) Virginia, a little American girl
January 15, 1927 (#2) Annette, Virginia's little French cousin
January 22, 1927 (#3) Therese, of Brittany
January 29, 1927 (#4) Ferdinand, of Madrid
February 5, 1927 (#5) Edward, of Great Britain
February 12, 1927 (#6) Douglas, of Scotland
February 19, 1927 (#7) Wilhelmina, of Holland
February 26, 1927 (#8) Sigurd, a boy of Norway
March 19, 1927 (#9) Linda, a little Swedish girl
April 2, 1927 (#10) Leon, of Russia
April 16, 1927 (#11) Catharina, of Rumania
April 30, 1927 (#12) Tony, a boy of Switzerland
Nov. 26, 1927 (#13) Ruzena, of Czecho-Slovakia
December 3, 1927 (#14) Mustapha, a boy of Turkey
January 7, 1928 (#15) Marco, of Greece
January 21, 1928 (#16) Ila, of Arabia
February 4, 1928 (#17) Rakai, of India
March 17, 1928 (#18) Sing Fat, a boy of Peking, China
April 28, 1928 (#19) Kato, of Japan
November 3, 1928 (#20) Iloila, of the Philippines
February 2, 1929 (#21) Lilui, of Hawaii
March 16, 1929 (#22) Pedro, of Mexico
March 30, 1929 (#23) Ikwa, an Eskimo boy from Alaska
April 13, 1929 (#24) Jack, a boy of Canada

January 8, 1927   **February 26, 1927**

November 3, 1928   April 13, 1929

Courtesy of Donna Brinkman

"Stitch With Love-Snip For Fun"
© November 7, 1964 *The Farmer*
(limited color; black, white and pink)
Courtesy of Wynn Yusas

**"The Farmer Girls
Go Swingin' Into Winter"**
© August 20, 1966 *The Farmer*
(limited color; black, white and pink)
Courtesy of Margaret Peiffer

"Sew For Your Busy-Body"
(in color)
© **March 1, 1969** *The Farmer*
Courtesy of Margaret Peiffer

"The Farmer Girls" (in color)
© **May 20, 1972** *The Farmer*
Courtesy of Margaret Peiffer

"Let's Play Paper Dolls" (in color)
© **July 16, 1983**
The Farmer/The Dakota Farmer
Courtesy of Margaret Peiffer

"Away In A Manger, No Crib For A Bed"
© **December, 1987** *The Farmer/The Dakota Farmer*

Pictures of paper maché figures were made into some clever stand-ups for this Christmas page. The paper maché figures belong to Margaret Peiffer (Associate Editor/Lifestyle of *The Farmer/The Dakota Farmer*) and have been in her family for more than 60 years. They were made in Germany. This page is also in full color.

Good Housekeeping

The *Good Housekeeping* magazine began in May 1885 in Holyoke, Massachusetts. The magazine celebrated its 100th anniversary just a few years ago in May 1985.

The following is a list of the known cut-out pages that have appeared in *Good Housekeeping* over the years. Pictures of those that contained paper dolls are shown following the list.

1909
February - "Little Louise and Her Pets"
April - "Little Louise's Sister May"
May - "Little Louise's Brother Ned"
September - "Little Louise's College Cousin"
October - "Little Louise's Friends – Cinderella"
November - "Little Louise's Friends – Rastus"

1911
January - The series, "Kinderkins," featured a paper doll with outfit patterns
December - "Rose Marie, Our New Portrait Dollie"

The following six pages contain cut-out toy dolls made to be fastened in such a way that they could move their heads, arms and legs. They did not come with extra outfits.

1918
December - "Write To Santa" (paper toy)

1919
January - "What Shall We Name The Children?" (paper toy)
February - "Ask Mother To Tell You The Story Of George Washington" (paper toy)
March - "And Here Is The Mother, Too" (paper toy)
April - "The Little Girl Is Named Polly" (paper toy)
May - "Peter Gives the May Queen A Handsome Bouquet" (paper toy)

"Polly Pratt Series"
October - "When Polly Pratt Came to Play – Of Course She Brought Her Doll" (two pages)
November - "Brother Ben and Baby Bess" (two pages)
December - "Sister Sallie and Cousin Sam – All You Need Is A Pair of Scissors" (two pages)

1920
January - (There was no magazine published this month)
February - "Polly Pratt Had A Valentine – Every Girl Should Have One" (two pages)
March - "This Is Polly Pratt's Sister Peggy – And This Young Man Is Brother Peter" (two pages)
April - "Polly Pratt Wanted A Baby Brother – Nurse Came To Help His Mother" (two pages)
May - "Polly Pratt Gave a May Day Party – Betty Brown Rode Over On Her Pony" (two pages)

June - "Polly Pratt Goes To A Vacation Camp – And Meets John and Janey Taylor" (two pages)

Note: The paper dolls are on one page from now on.
July/August - "Polly Pratt's Little Country Cousin"
September - "Polly Pratt's New Friends At School"
October - "Polly Pratt Gives A Halloween Party"
November - "Polly Goes To Grandma's For Thanksgiving"
December - "Polly Pratt's Christmas Caller"

1921
January - "Polly's Neighbors Come To Play"
February - "Polly Gives a Fancy Dress Party"
March - "Polly's Pretty School Teacher"
April - "Polly Pratt's Easter Visitors"
May - "Polly Pratt Gives a Doll Party"
June - "Polly's Sister Has a June Wedding"
July - "Polly Has A Fourth of July Picnic"
August - "Polly Visits Friends At The Seashore"

"The Kiddyland Movie Cut-Outs" ran consecutively from September 1921 to August 1923 for a total of 24 issues. The pages were very colorful. At the top of the page was the theater (or movie screen) and the movie "film" was at the bottom of the page. The film consisted of four or five strips of paper which were to be cut and joined together and then pulled through the theater screen at the top of the page. One example of the "Kiddyland Movies" is shown.

1923
October - "Little Maryjane"
November - "Sister Priscilla"
December - "Marjorie From Across The Street"

1924
January - "Nancy And Her New Skates"
February - "May I Be Your Valentine?"
March - "Polly And Her Puppy"
April - "Miriam Has a Happy Easter"
May - "Little Ellen Is Queen Of the May Party"
June - "Ann Goes to The Sunday School Picnic"
July - "Alice Spends July on Grandma's Farm"
August - "Betty Goes To The Beach In August"
September - "This Is the Way Ruth Goes To School"
October - "Caroline Goes To China"

November - "Bonnie Bessie Lives in Scotland"
December - "Katrinka, The Little Russian"

1925
January - "Hildegarde Lives In Holland"
February - "Sonya, The Little Gipsy"
March - "Thelma, Who Lives In Sweden"

An advertising paper doll page appeared in March 1948, April 1951 and April 1952. These pages will be pictured at the back of the book with other advertising paper dolls.
A series of cut-out pages by Joan Walsh Anglund began in February 1978. These pages are listed below but are not pictured. If no title was included on the page, a short description is given.

1978
February - "Will You Be My Valentine?" (paper doll)
March - Directions for making a "bunny" mask for Easter
October - "October Children's Page" (Halloween mobile)
December - "Christmas Is A Special Time" (paper doll)

1979
February - "February Children's Page" (valentines)
April - "Let's Make An Easter Shoe-Box Scene"
October - "October Children's Page – Halloween Is Coming!" (paper doll)
December - "It's December ... The Merriest Month Of The Year!" (Christmas ornaments)

1980
February - "Finger Puppet Show For Valentine's Day"
April - "Happy Easter" (Easter egg holders)
September - "Almost A Rainbow" (illustrated quotations)
October - "Happy Halloween" (paper toy)
December - "A Christmas Doll For Mother" (directions for making a stuffed doll)

1981
February - "Happy Valentine's Day" (valentines)
April - "Little Polly" (paper doll with Easter bonnets)
May - "For A Dear Mother" (a poem for Mother's Day)
September - "Love One Another" (poster)
October - "It's Halloween" (centerpiece)
December - "Merry Christmas" (paper dolls)

1982
February - "Happy Valentine's Day" (valentines)
April - "A Happy Easter Game For You"

October - Halloween picture with instructions for making a jigsaw puzzle.
December - Christmas scene and poem

1983
February - Valentine bookmarks
April - "Happy Easter – Let's Make An Easter Egg Tree"
October - "Halloween" (decorations and game suggestions)
December - "Christmas From A To Z" (three pages of 26 illustrated alphabet blocks from A to Z)

1984
February - Valentines
April - "An Easter Paper Doll For You"
September - "God Is Love" (illustrated quotations)
October - "Halloween Finger Puppets" (five puppet cut-outs and pumpkin theater)
December - Nativity scene with stand-up figures

1985
February - Valentines
April - "Let's Make An Easter Mobile"
October - "Let's Give A ... Halloween Party!" (stand-up place cards)
December - "Santa's Favorite Oatmeal Cookies" (a recipe)

1986
February - "A Special Valentine Doll" (a paper toy doll that will move)
March - "Happy Easter" (paper dolls)
October - "Happy Halloween" (Halloween cards)
December - "Merry Christmas" (Christmas decorations)

1987
February - "Happy Valentine's Day 1987" (paper doll)
April - "Easter 1987 – An Easter Hunt" (a picture and word hunt)
October - "Happy Halloween!" (paper dolls)
December - Gift tags

1988
February - "Happy Valentine's Day 1988" (valentines)
April - "Happy Easter" (directions for making an Easter Bunny vase)
October - "Happy Halloween" (paper dolls with masks)
December - "Christmas Is Love" (two pages of illustrated verses)

1989
February - "Happy Valentine"s Day" (directions for a valentine cake)
April - "Happy Easter" (paper dolls)

February 1909

April 1909

May 1909

September 1909

All *Good Housekeeping* paper dolls are from the collection of Virginia Crossley.

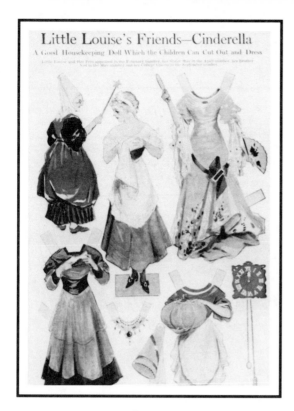

October 1909

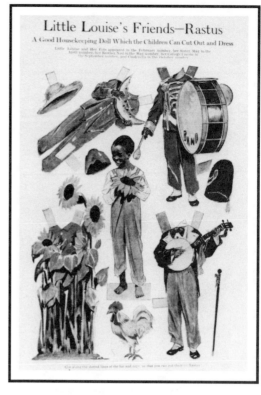

November 1909

December 1911

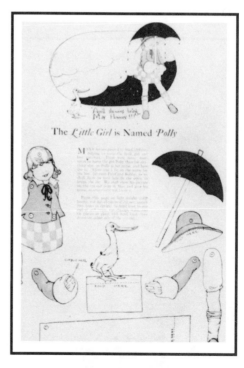

April 1919
This is an example of the paper toy series that ran from December 1918 to May 1919.

The following "Polly Pratt" series was presented on two pages in the magazine through June 1920.

October 1919

November 1919

December 1919

February 1920

March 1920

April 1920

May 1920

June 1920

The "Polly Pratt" series continues but now only on one page.

July/August 1920

September 1920

October 1920

November 1920

December 1920

January 1921

February 1921

March 1921

April 1921

May 1921

June 1921

July 1921

August 1921
(The last of the "Polly Pratt" Series)

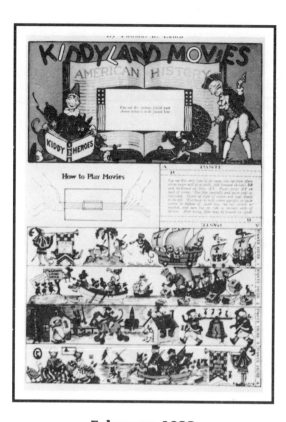

February 1922
This is an example of the "Kid-dyland Movie Cut-Outs" that ran from September 1921 to August 1923.

October 1923

November 1923

December 1923

January 1924

February 1924

March 1924

April 1924

June 1924

May 1924

July 1924

August 1924

September 1924

October 1924

November 1924

December 1924

January 1925

February 1925

March 1925

The Grade Teacher

The Grade Teacher had its beginnings back in 1885 when it was known as *Popular Educator*. In 1926, *Popular Educator* united with *Primary Education*, and the two magazines became known as *Primary Education – Popular Educator* until February 1929. In March of that year, the name was changed to *The Grade Teacher*. The name was changed to *The Teacher* in 1972, and then in 1981 it became *Instructor and Teacher* when it merged with *Instructor*.

The May 1930 issue contains an article titled, "Paper Dolls That Teach Manners," but paper dolls are not included in the article. In the January 1933 issue, there is an ad for *Pictorial Review* showing a paper doll of "Dolly Dingle." *The Grade Teacher* was checked from the first issue in March 1929 through June 1957, and many of these issues contained paper toys and stand-up figures. The paper dolls that were found are pictured herein.

These first two paper dolls continue the series that was started in the forerunner *Primary Education – Popular Educator*.

April 1929
"Little Neighbors Across The Ocean"
Terry and his Irish Costume - Highland Molly and her Kiltie Suit.

June 1929
"Canadian Maid and her Evangeline Costume - Canadian Boy and his Champlain Costume."

All paper dolls in *The Grade Teacher* are in black and white.

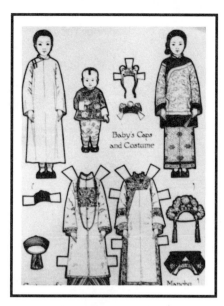

June 1933
"Chinese Costumes"

September 1940
"Pussy Goes To Market"

November 1945
"Jack and Jane Play Pilgrim"

September 1946
"Rusty and Dusty
Get Ready For School"

December 1940
"Miss America"

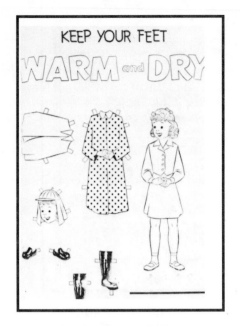

September 1950
"Keep Your Feet
Warm and Dry"

September 1951
"Figures For Your Table Exhibit
Children of Bolivia and Peru"

The Home Friend Magazine

The Home Friend Magazine was published monthly by the United Publishing Co. in Kansas City, Missouri. The July 1932 issue shown was Volume 29 No. 4 and contained just 12 pages. Subscription rates were 25¢ a year. A paper doll with a Martha Washington costume was included in the July 1932 issue. Extra costumes for the doll appeared in the following months.

July 1932 cover of *The Home Friend Magazine*
Courtesy of Helen Johnson

The Housekeeper

The Housekeeper was published by The Housekeeper Corporation from 1877 to February 1911 at which time it was purchased by Mr. Robert Collier (publisher of *Colliers Magazine*) and Mr. Conde Nast (publisher of *Vogue*). The magazine was published by Collier and Nast, Inc. until early 1913 when it was sold to the McClure Publications, Inc. (publisher of *McClure's Magazine* and *The Ladies World*). *The Housekeeper* was consolidated with *The Ladies World* at that time and then was called *The Ladies World and Housekeeper*.

The following issues of *The Housekeeper* were checked for paper dolls; November 1907 to October 1908 (volume #31), no paper dolls were found. The next volume (#32) covered November 1908 to October 1909. Some issues were missing including February 1909 which is thought to contain this magazine's first paper doll page "The Sonbonnet Babies Have Come To Play With You." This page then could not be verified or pictured. The remaining volumes #33 to #36 (November 1909 until the end in 1913) were also checked for paper dolls and those found are pictured.

**March 1909
"The Jolly Overall Boys Have
Come To Play With You"
Courtesy of Helen Johnson**

**April 1909
"The Sonbonnet Babies Are
Playing Dress Up This Month"**

May 1909
"Overall Boys Camping Out"
Courtesy of Helen Johnson

June 1909
"The Sunbonnet Babies Are
Taking Care Of The Children"

October 1909
"The Jolly Overall Boys
Are With Us Again"
Courtesy of Helen Johnson

November 1909
"The Jolly Overall Boys
Are Ready For Thanksgiving"
Courtesy of Donna Heiser

December 1909
"The Christmas Sunbonnet Babies"

January 1910
"The Jolly Overall Boys"

March 1910
"The Sunbonnet Babies
In Fancy Dress"

September 1910
"The Sunbonnet Babies
Are With Us Again"
Courtesy of Rosalie Eppert

November 1910
"The Jolly Overall Boys
Are With Us Again"

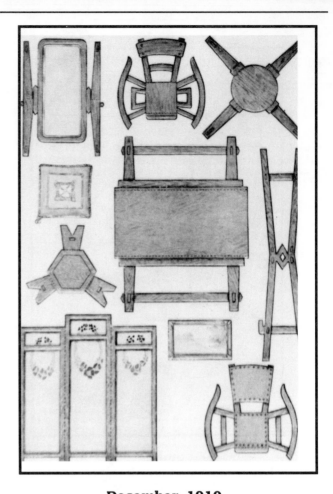

December 1910
"Furniture For The Doll's House"
(sitting room)
Courtesy of Rosalie Eppert
This is one example of furniture
pages that appeared in *The Housekeeper.* Others appeared in August
and October 1910 and June 1911.

January 1911
"The Sunbonnet Babies
Are With Us Again"

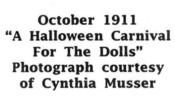

October 1911
"A Halloween Carnival
For The Dolls"
Photograph courtesy
of Cynthia Musser

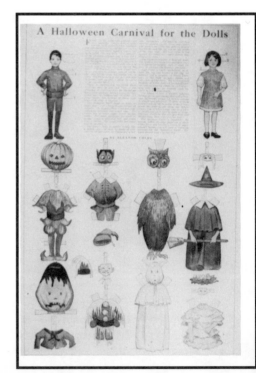

Judge Magazine

Judge Magazine was published in New York from 1881 to January 1939. *Leslie's* which began as *Leslie's Illustrated Weekly Newspaper* in New York in 1855 merged with *Judge Magazine* in 1922.

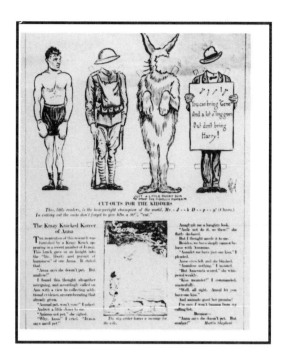

August 1925
"Cut-Outs For the Kidders"
(Jack Dempsey)
Courtesy of Norene Allen

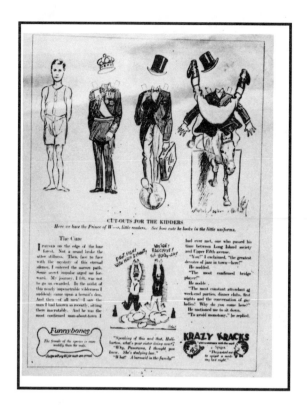

September 1925
"Cut-Outs For the Kidders"
(Prince of Wales)
Courtesy of Norene Allen

"Cut-Outs For the Kidders"
Date not verified
(William Randolph Hearst)
Courtesy of Norene Allen

"Cut-Outs For the Kidders"
Date not verified
(Will Hays)
Courtesy of Carol Carey

Two other "Cut-Outs For The Kidders" that are known to exist are "William Jennings Bryan" and "Calvin Coolidge," precise dates unknown.

June 1937
"Grownup Cutouts John L. Lewis"

July 1937
"Grownup Cutouts"

Junior Instructor Magazine, Junior Home Magazine

The *Junior Instructor Magazine* was known as the "Home Edition" of the *Normal Instructor and Primary Plans* magazine. Both were published by F.A. Owen Publishing Co. and contained similar material, but the *Junior Instructor Magazine* was adapted for home use as well as for the school room. November 1919 was the first issue. The ownership of the *Junior Instructor Magazine* was transferred in January 1922 from the F.A. Owen Publishing Co. to the D.C. Kreidler Co. of Chicago. Three months later the name of the magazine was changed to *Junior Home Magazine.* Features from *Normal Instructor and Primary Plans* continued to be used in *Junior Home Magazine* with full cooperation of the former publishers. Beginning with the first issue of *Junior Instructor Magazine* many paper toys and stand-up figures were featured. A nice paper doll series started in October 1920 by Florence England Nosworthy followed by other paper dolls through the years. The D.C. Kreidler Co. published a thick book in 1923 titled *The Bizzy-Wizzy Book For Juniors* which included many of the cut-out pages from the above magazines including some of the paper doll pages.

In 1926, the magazine *Little Folks* combined with *Junior Home Magazine,* and in August 1932 the title was changed to *Junior Home For Parent and Child.* In April 1935, there was another name change to *Junior Home For Mothers,* and in 1936 the magazine ended when it merged with *Parents' Magazine.*

**Junior Instructor Magazine
Front cover of the
first issue November 1919.**

A pattern for a muslin doll "Baby Blossom" appeared in the July/August issue of *The Junior Instructor* in 1920.

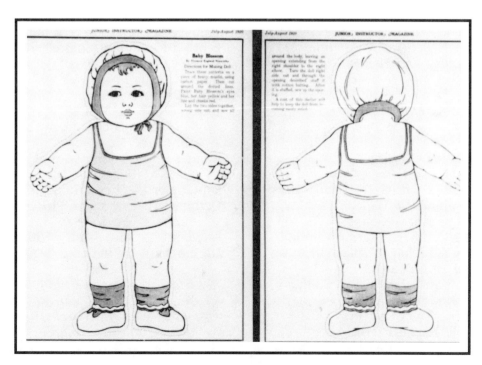

The following is a list of the paper dolls found in *Junior Instructor Magazine* and *Junior Home Magazine*. Some paper doll pages were not available to photograph.

1920
October - "Judy Herself"
November - "Judy's Twin, Jimmy"
December - "Judy on Christmas Day"

1921
January - "Jimmy and His Snow Man"
January - "Here Are Goldilocks and Her Three Bears" (a cut-out page with four paper dolls that have movable arms and legs. Includes one outfit for Goldilocks.)
February - "Judy Goes To A Valentine Party"
March - "Jimmy At Play"
April - "Farmer Boy Jimmy"
May - "Judy In May"
June - "Judy Attends A June Wedding"
July - "Jimmy's Fourth of July"
August - "Judy's Vacation"
September - "Judy Goes To School"
October - "Bobby's Colonial Costume"
November - "Betty's Colonial Costume"
December - "Little Dutch Elsa"

1922
January - "Bobby's Dutch Costume"
February - "Betty's Highland Costume"
March - "Bobby's Highland Costume"

Junior Home Magazine *Begins With The April Issue*
April - "Betty's Japanese Costume"
May - "Bobby As A Jolly Little Japanese Boy"
June - "Betty As A Spanish Girl"
July - "Bobby's Spanish Costume"
August - "Betty In Bohemian Costume"
September - "Bobby's Bohemian Costume"
October - "Dotty Daisy and Her Fall Clothes"
November - "Barbara May – Dotty Daisy's Best Friend"
December - "Barbara's Brother Peter"

1923
January - "Dotty Daisy's Mother"
February - "Dotty Daisy's Father" (included on the page are three outfits for "Dotty Daisy," "Barbara May" and "Peter")
March - "Dotty Daisy's Baby Sister"
April - "Dotty Daisy and Her Spring Clothes"
April - The "Juniors' Exchange" page includes a paper doll and three outfits.
May - "Barbara May and Her Spring Clothes"
June - "Peter and His Friend Bill"
July - "Dotty Daisy"s Twin Cousins"
August - "The Little Friend At the Seashore"
September - "Jimmy – A Little School Friend"

October - Paper doll of a small boy named "Teddy" (favorite cousin of Dotty Daisy)
November - "'Heide' A Little Swiss Girl"
December - "Hans Brinker"

1924
January - "Alice In Wonderland"
February - "Little Lord Fauntleroy"
March - "Understood Betsy"
April - "Little Black Sambo"
May - "Cinderella"
June - "Nat" From Little Women"
July - "Mytyl From 'The Blue Bird' "
August - "Peter Pan"
September - "Phronsie"
October - "Hiawatha"
November - "Black Beauty"
December - "Mary 'The Christmas Angel' "

1925
January - "Nelly's Silver Mine"
February - "Old Mother Goose"
March - "Little Tommy Tucker"
April - "Mary, Mary Quite Contrary"
May - "Little Jack Horner"
June - "The Queen Of Hearts"
July - "Jack"
August - "Jill"
September - "Peter, Peter, Pumpkin Eater"
October - "Little Miss Muffet"
November - "Little Boy Blue"
December - no paper dolls

1926
January - "Polly, Put The Kettle On"
February - "Bobby Shafto"
March - "Little Bo Peep"
April - "Willy, Willy, Wilkin"
May - "Where Are You Going My Pretty Maid?"
June - "Jack Be Nimble"
July - "Curly Locks! Curly Locks! Wilt Thou Be Mine?"
August - "As Tommy Snooks and Bessie Brooks Were Walking Out On Sunday"
September - "There Was A Little Girl"
October - "Peter Piper Picked A Peck of Pickled Peppers"
November - "Little Polly Flinders"
December - No paper dolls

A series of six advertising paper dolls for Fels-Naptha Soap began in October 1927 and ended with the March 1928 issue. An example of one of these pages will be found in the back of this book with other advertising pa-

per dolls.
The only other paper dolls found are listed below:

1930

November - "Donald and Dotty – The Tidy Twins. Dolls For Creative Poster Work" (Also in this issue is an article titled "Colonial Toys" which contains patterns for a little boy and girl, clothes and animals.)

1931

May - "Paper Dolls For Your Doll House"

Most of the remaining issues through December 1932 contained paper toys but issues after that, until Junior Home Magazine *ended in 1936, could not be found for research.*
All paper dolls in Junior Instructor Magazine *and* Junior Home Magazine *are in black and white.*

October 1920

November 1920

December 1920

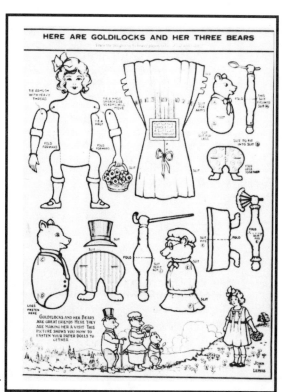

January 1921

January 1921

February 1921

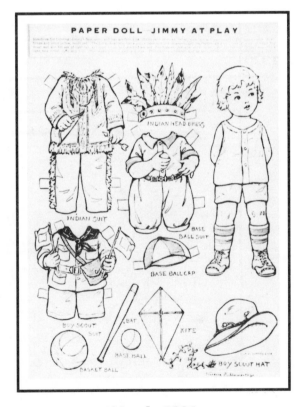

March 1921

April 1921

May 1921

June 1921

July 1921

August 1921

September 1921

October 1921

November 1921

December 1921

January 1922

February 1922

March 1922
The *Junior Instructor Magazine* page of "Bobby's Highland Costume" was not available. Shown is the identical page with a different title from *The Bizzy Wizzy Book.*
Courtesy of Patti Fertel

April 1922
(**With this issue the magazine is now called** *Junior Home Magazine.*)

May 1922

June 1922

July 1922
The *Junior Home Magazine* page of "Bobby's Spanish Costume" was not available. Shown is the identical page with a different title from *The Bizzy Wizzy Book*.
Courtesy of Patti Fertel

August 1922
The *Junior Home Magazine* page of "Betty in Bohemian Costume" was not available. Shown is the identical page with a different title from *The Bizzy Wizzy Book*.
Courtesy of Rosalie Eppert

September 1922
The *Junior Home Magazine* page of "Bobby's Bohemian Costume" was not available. Shown is the identical page with a different title from *The Bizzy Wizzy Book*.
Courtesy of Patti Fertel.

October 1922

November 1922

December 1922

January 1923

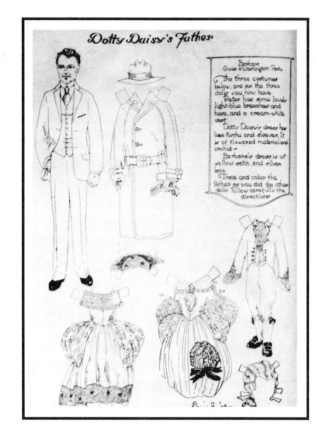

February 1923

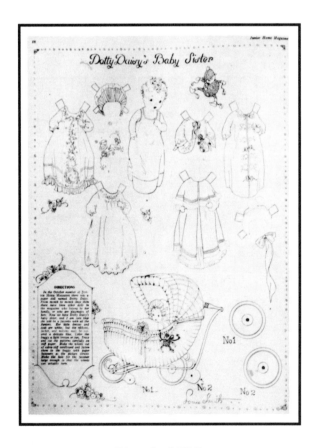

March 1923

April 1923

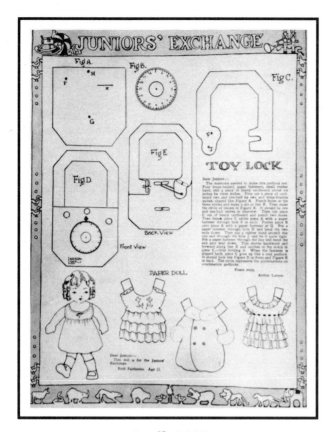

April 1923

May 1923

October 1923
Courtesy of Rosalie Eppert

November 1923

**January 1924
Courtesy of Helen Johnson**

**February 1924
Courtesy of Helen Johnson**

**March 1924
Courtesy of Helen Johnson**

**April 1924
Courtesy of Helen Johnson**

May 1924
Courtesy of Helen Johnson

July 1924
Courtesy of Helen Johnson

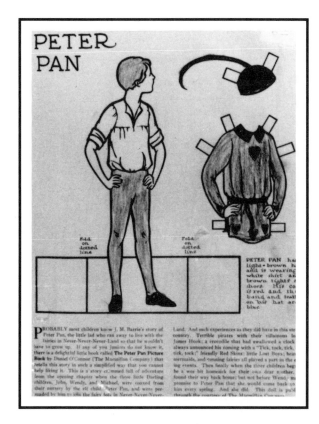

August 1924

September 1924

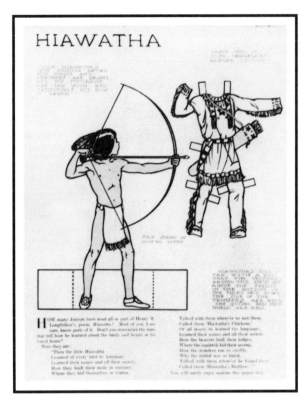

October 1924
Courtesy of Helen Johnson

November 1924
Courtesy of Helen Johnson

December 1924
Courtesy of Helen Johnson

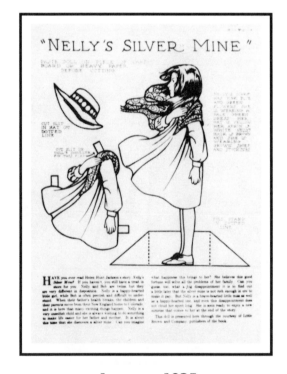

January 1925

August 1925
Courtesy of Rosalie Eppert

September 1925
Courtesy of Rosalie Eppert

February 1926

April 1926
Courtesy of Madeline Smith

May 1926
Courtesy of Rosalie Eppert

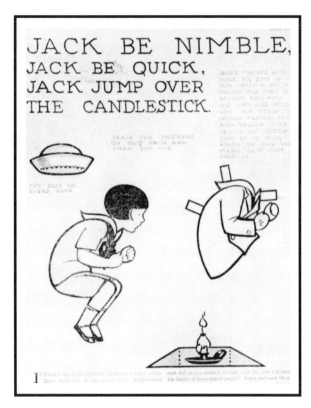

June 1926
Courtesy of Madeline Smith

July 1926
Courtesy of Madeline Smith

August 1926

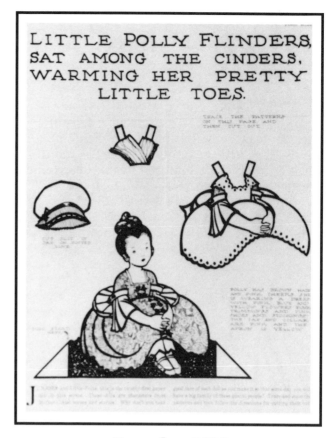

October 1926

November 1926
Courtesy of Rosalie Eppert

November 1930
Courtesy of Helen Johnson

May 1931

Ladies' Home Journal

The Ladies' Home Journal (incorporating The Home Journal) began in 1883 and was a monthly, although there was at least one period, from September 1910 to May 1911, when it came out twice a month. The earliest known paper dolls featured in this magazine is a series of "Lettie Lane" paper dolls which began in October 1908.

The following is a list of all known paper dolls and paper toys found in The Ladies' Home Journal beginning with October 1908. The paper doll pages are pictured at the end of the list.

Cover of January 1915
Ladies' Home Journal

1908
"The Lettie Lane Paper Family"
October - This page introduces Miss Lettie Lane
November - "Introducing Lettie's Little Twin Brother and Sister"
December - "Presenting Lettie's Grandmother, Who Brings Christmas Presents To Lettie"

1909
January - "Presenting Lettie's Baby Sister, With Her Nurse and Some Of Her Belongings"
February - "Presenting Lettie's Mother and Several Of Her Costumes"
March - "Presenting Lettie's Sister As A Bride"
April - "Presenting Lettie's Father, Who Is A Man Of Fashion"
May - "Presenting Lettie's Best Friend And Some Of Her Pretty Dresses"
June - "Presenting Lettie's Brother, With His Clothes and His Playthings"
July - "Presenting One Of Lettie's Dolls, With Her Hats and Dresses"
August - "Presenting Lettie's Lady Doll, Her Maid, and Some Of Her Fashionable Dresses"
September - "Presenting Lettie's Dolls' Party Of Little People Dressed In Fancy Costumes"

A New Series Presenting Lettie's Sister's Wedding
November - "The Bridegroom"
December - "The Maid of Honor"

1910
January - "The Minister and The Best Man"
February - "Lettie's Sister's Bridesmaids"
March - "The Flower Girls"
April - "Some Of The Wedding Guests"
May - "The Youngest Wedding Guest"

"Lettie Lane's Around-The-World Party"
July - Japanese Girl and a Japanese Boy
August - Chinese Girl and a Chinese Boy

September 1 - Russian Girl and a Russian Boy
October 1 - Norwegian Girl and Boy and Their Nurse
November 1 - German Girl and some German Costumes
December 1 - Austrian Girl and Boy
December 15 - Two Little Swiss Girls

1911
January 1 - Italian Boy and Girl
February 1 - Spanish Boy and Girl
March 1 - French Girl and a Punch and Judy Show
March 15 - "The Doll That Has Come To Life" (not with this series)
April 1 - A Boy and Girl of The Netherlands
April 15 - "Lettie Lane's Most Beautiful Doll As A Bride" (not with this series)
May 1 - Scotch Boy and an Irish Girl
June - Little American Girl
This ends the series of "Lettie Lane's Around-The-World Party"
July - "Lettie Lane's Doll In Her Vacation Clothes"
August - "Lettie's Sewing Box" (this is just a small article)
October - "Lettie Lane's Doll In Her School Clothes"
October - "A Three-Fold Halloween Party Idea"

(place-cards)

December - "Lettie Lane's Most Beautiful Doll – In Her Party Clothes"

December - "A Christmas Tree For The Dolls" (toys and ornaments to put on stand-up tree)

December - "A Christmas Dinner For The Dolls" (dishes and food to cut out)

The pages above that feature "Lettie Lane's Doll" (March 15, April 15, July, October and December) are not actual paper doll pages. The doll pictured is a "real" doll and the outfits shown are dresses made from patterns to fit the doll. The doll and patterns were given away free for three-year subscriptions to The Ladies' Home Journal.

1912

July - "Flossie Fisher's Funnies" (a black and white page)

October - "Children's Cut-Out Paper Parties Of the Stories They Love Best: I – Cinderella"

November - "Lettie Lane's Doll House" (not a cut-out page)

December - "Lettie Lane's Doll House" (not a cut-out page and in black and white)

The doll house shown in the above two issues was given away with three-year subscriptions to The Ladies' Home Journal.

December - "The Children's Toy Shop" (cut-out toys to be used in a miniature toy shop)

1913

February - "Children's Cut-Out Paper Parties Of the Stories They Love Best: II – Goldilocks"

June - "Children's Cut-Out Paper Parties Of the Stories They Love Best: III – Jack and the Beanstalk"

"A Cut-Out Circus For the Children"

June - "Part I – The Grand Review" (stand-up figures)

July - "Part II – The Performance Act I" (stand-up figures)

August - "Part III – The Performance Act II" (stand-up figures plus clown and outfits)

September - "Part IV – The Wild West Show" (stand-up figures)

October - "Part V – The Side Show" (stand-up figures)

November - "Part VI – The Menagerie" (stand-up figures)

This ends the "Circus" pages.

December - "The Mother Goose Christmas Tree" (stand-up figures)

1914

January - "The Kiddies' Koasting Karnival" (stand-up figures)

February - "Mount Vernon, The Home of George Washington" (Self-Made Pictures For Children's Rooms)

March - "The White House" (Self-Made Pictures For Children's Rooms)

April - "Ann Hathaway's Cottage" (Self-Made Pictures For Children's Rooms)

May - "Niagara Falls" (Self-Made Pictures For Children's Rooms)

June - "The Steeplechase" (stand-up figures)

September - "Longfellow's Home" (Self-Made Pictures For Children's Rooms)

October - "Children's Cut-Out Paper Parties Of the Stories They Love Best – Alice In Wonderland"

November - "Windsor Castle" (Self-Made Pictures for Children's Rooms)

December - "The Children's Christmas Tree In Independence Square, Philadelphia" (same format as Self-Made pictures for Children's Rooms)

December - "The Night Before Christmas"

1915

January - "Lettie Lane Comes Home For Christmas"

February - "Arlington: When It Was The Home Of General Robert E. Lee" (Self-Made Pictures For Children's Rooms)

March - "Lettie Lane Introduces Betty Bonnet"

April - "Venice, The Pearl of the Adriatic" (Self-Made Pictures For Children's Rooms)

May - "Lettie Lane Introduces Billy Bonnet"

June - "The United States Capitol At Washington" (Self-Made Pictures For Children's Rooms")

July - "Lettie Lane Introduces Betty Bonnet's Little Sister and Her Nurse"

September - "Betty Bonnet's College Sister"

October - "Washington's Headquarters At Valley Forge" (Self-Made Pictures For Children's Rooms)

November - "Betty Bonnet's Brother Bob"

November - "Paper Furniture For Your Betty Bonnet Doll" (dining room and bedroom)

December - "Paper Furniture For Your Betty Bonnet Doll" (kitchen, living room, hallway)

The two paper furniture pages above are in black and white.

December - "The Good Wish Letter" (cut-out presents to be used in a Christmas letter)

1916

February - "Betty Bonnet's Boarding School Sister"

March - "Betty Bonnet's Father and Mother"

April - "Betty Bonnet's Best Friend"

May - "Betty Bonnet's Next-Door Neighbor"

June - "Betty Bonnet's Dearest Dolls"

July - "Betty Bonnet's Twin Cousins"

September - "Betty Bonnet's Married Sister"

October - "Betty Bonnet's Sister's Baby"

November - "Betty Bonnet's Little Niece"

December - "Betty Bonnet's Christmas Party"

1917
January - "Betty Bonnet's Sister's Son"
February - "Betty Bonnet's Camp Fire Cousin"
March - "Betty Bonnet's Country Cousins"
April - "Betty Bonnet's Teacher" (black and white page)
May - "Betty Bonnet's Big Brother"
June - "Betty Bonnet's College Cousins"
July - "Betty Bonnet's Patriotic Party"
September - "Betty Bonnet's Grandparents Now and Long Ago"
October - "Betty Bonnet's Halloween Party"
November - "Betty Bonnet's Army and Navy Cousins"
December - "Betty Bonnet Shops Early"

1918
January - "Betty Bonnet's New Year's Callers"
February - "Betty Bonnet's Valentine"
March - "Betty Bonnet's Household Servants"
April - "Betty Bonnet's Rainy Day Party"
May - "Betty Bonnet's May Basket"
June - "Betty Bonnet Goes To A Wedding – The Bride"
July - "Betty Bonnet Goes To A Wedding – The Bridegroom"
September - "Betty Bonnet Goes To A Wedding – The Page and The Flower Girl"
This ends the "Betty Bonnet" paper dolls.
October - "Peggy Perkins, Your New Playmate" (black and white page)
November - "Peggy Perkins' Friend, Margie Martin" (black and white page)
December - "Peggy Perkins' Tree and Her Presents" (black and white page)

1919
January - "Peggy Perkins' Brother Bobby" (black and white page)

1920
September - "Robinson Crusoe"
October - "Halloween Party Place Cards" (stand-up figures)

The following is a series of nine pages of stand-up figures by Harrison Cady.
November - "The Woodland School"
December - "Little Mr. Squirrel's Christmas Party"

1921
January - "Li'l Bobby Bear and the Snowbirds' Sleigh Ride"
February - "Johnny Funny Bunny and the Tadpole Baby"
March - "Ol' Mister Turtle and the Mischievous Minnow"

April - "The Musical Triumph of Mr. Thaddeus Toad"
May - "Johnny Funny Bunny's Spring Planting"
June - "The Coming-Out Party of Betty Butterfly"
December - "How Old Mr. Long-Tail Became Santa Claus"
This ends the Harrison Cady series.

1922
January - "The Dutch Twins and the Storks"
February - "The Mexican Twins Celebrate San Ramon's Day"
March - "The French Twins"
April - "The Eskimo Twins"
May - "The Spartan Twins"
June - "The Japanese Twins"
July - "The Scotch Twins"
August - "The Italian Twins"
September - "The Irish Twins"
October - "The Belgian Twins"
November - "The Puritan Twins"
December - "The Cave Twins"

1923
January - "When the Snow Man Sat By The Fire"
February - "St. Valentine's Day In Pudding Lane"
March - "Jack and Jill and Bumbo the Bear"
April - "Simple Simon Has His Day"
May - "Mrs. Claus and the King of France"
June - "The Poodle That Didn't Know English"
July - "Little Bo-Peep and the Dutch Uncle"
August - "Little Boy Blue and the Little Girl With the Curl"
September - "Little Miss Muffet and Taffy the Welshman"
October - "Santa Claus and Judy"
November - "The Discontent of Mrs. Pumpkin-Eater"
Beginning with the December 1923 issue, a series of cut-out scenes titled "The Gimmicks" ran consecutively through May 1925.

1939
September - "Make Your Little Girl Dresses From These Hollywood Paper-Doll Cut Outs" (two pages)

1940
September - "A School Wardrobe For You and Your Doll"

1947
September - "As Back To School I Go"

1948
April - "Mrs. Hogan's One-Dress Wardrobe"
May - "It's All In The Family" (two pages)

October 1908

November 1908

December 1908

January 1909
Courtesy of Virginia Crossley

February 1909
Courtesy of Virginia Crossley

March 1909

April 1909

May 1909

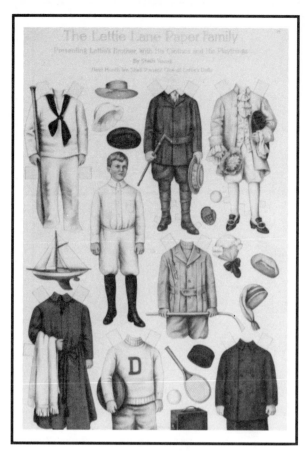

June 1909

July 1909
Courtesy of Virginia Crossley

August 1909

September 1909

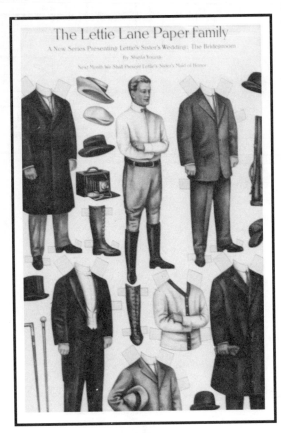

November 1909

December 1909

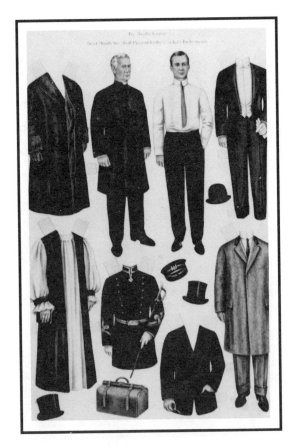

January 1910

February 1910

March 1910

April 1910

May 1910

July 1910

August 1910

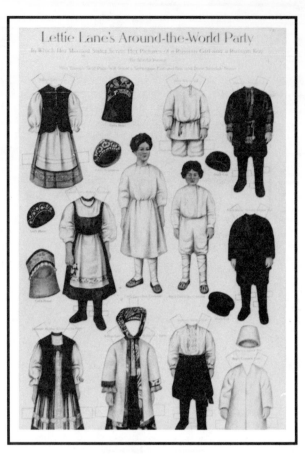

September 1, 1910

October 1, 1910

November 1, 1910

December 1, 1910

December 15, 1910
Courtesy of Virginia Crossley

January 1, 1911

February 1, 1911

March 1, 1911

March 15, 1911
Courtesy of Virginia Crossley

April 1, 1911

April 15, 1911

May 1, 1911

June 1911

July 1911

October 1911

December 1911
Courtesy of Virginia Crossley

July 1912
Courtesy of Virginia Crossley

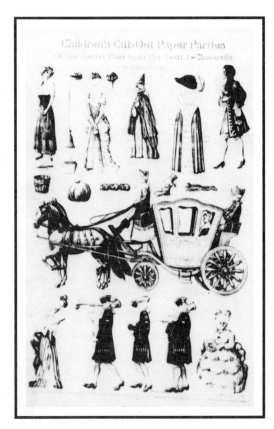

October 1912
Courtesy of Donna Heiser

February 1913

June 1913

September 1913
This is just one of six beautiful circus pages that came out in 1913. However, this is the only one that had a paper doll with outfits.

October 1914
Courtesy of Donna Heiser

December 1914

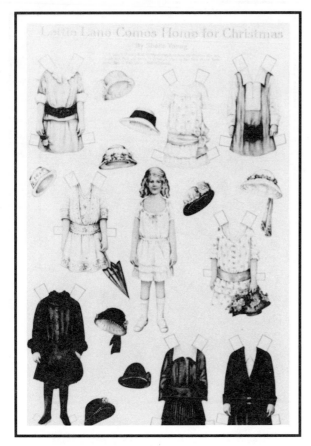

January 1915

March 1915

May 1915

July 1915

September 1915

November 1915

Nonvember 1915

December 1915

February 1916

March 1916

April 1916

May 1916

June 1916

July 1916

September 1916

October 1916

November 1916
Courtesy of Virginia Crossley

December 1916

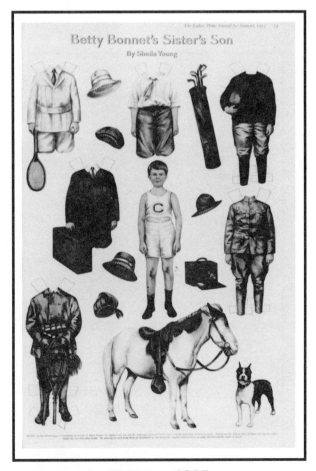

January 1917

February 1917

March 1917

April 1917

May 1917

June 1917

July 1917

September 1917

October 1917

November 1917

December 1917

January 1918

February 1918

March 1918

April 1918

May 1918

June 1918

July 1918

September 1918

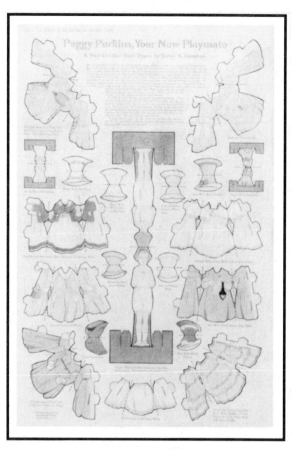

October 1918
Courtesy of Virginia Crossley

November 1918

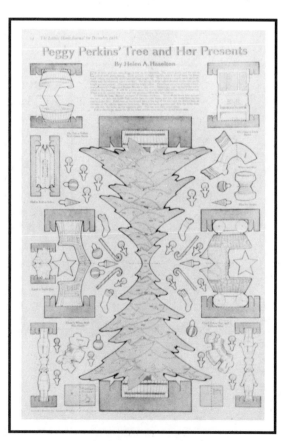

December 1918
Courtesy of Virginia Crossley

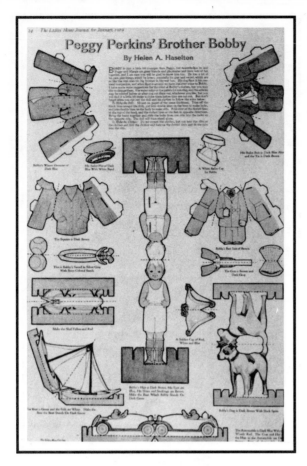

January 1919

September 1920

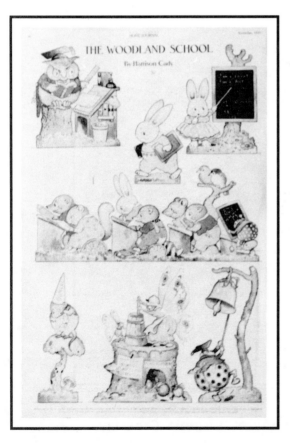

November 1920
This is one example of the series of stand-up figures by Harrison Cady that appeared in 1920 and 1921.

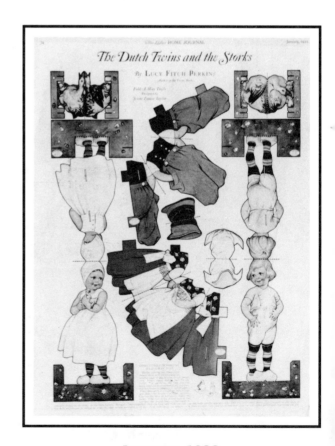

January 1922

February 1922

March 1922

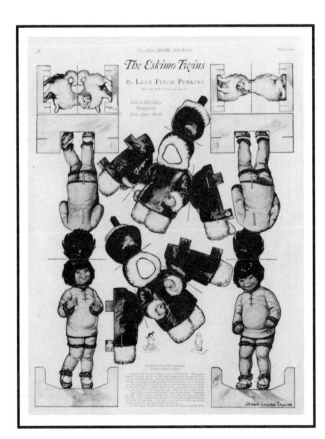

April 1922

May 1922

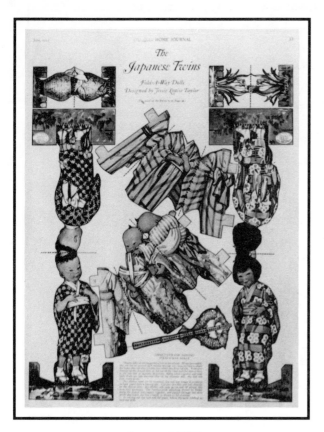

June 1922

July 1922

August 1922

September 1922

October 1922

November 1922

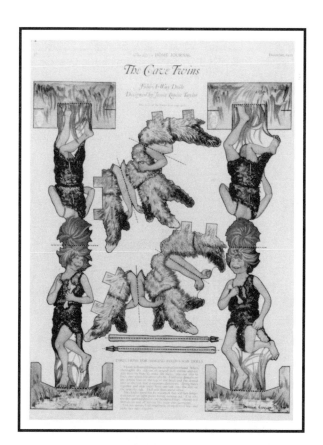

December 1922
Courtesy of Virginia Crossley

January 1923

February 1923
Courtesy of Virginia Crossley

March 1923
Courtesy of Virginia Crossley

April 1923

May 1923

June 1923

July 1923
Courtesy of Virginia Crossley

August 1923
Courtesy of Virginia Crossley

September 1923

October 1923
Courtesy of Virginia Crossley

November 1923

December 1923
This is one example of "The Gimmicks" series that ran from December 1923 through May 1925.

September 1939

September 1940

September 1947
Courtesy of Virginia Crossley

April 1948

May 1948

Ladies' World

Ladies' World was published in New York from January 1880 to January 1918. *The House-keeper* merged with *Ladies' World* in 1913. The paper dolls pictured are the only known paper dolls from this magazine.

Paper dolls on this page are courtesy of Rosalie Eppert.

**September 1916
"The First of Our Movie Dolls
Mary Pickford"**

**October 1916
"The Second of Our Movie Dolls
Billie Burke"**

**November 1916
"Our Third Movie Doll
Marguerite Clark"**

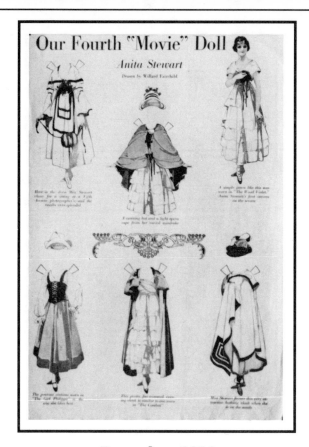

December 1916
"Our Fourth Movie Doll Anita Stewart"
Courtesy of Rosalie Eppert

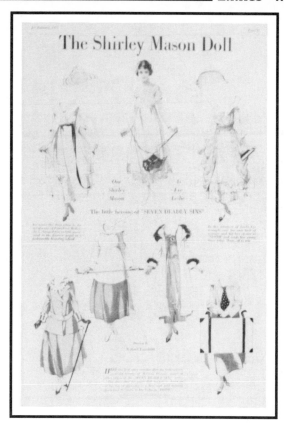

January 1917
"The Shirley Mason Doll"
Courtesy of Rosalie Eppert

February 1917
"Our Sixth Movie Doll
Marie Doro"
Courtesy of Rosalie Eppert

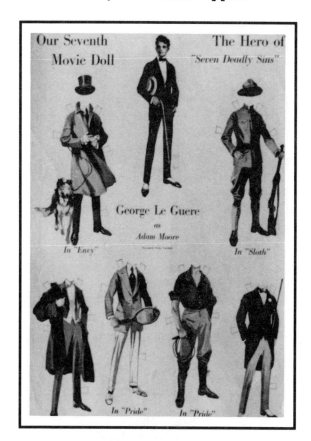

March 1917
"Our Seventh Movie Doll
George Le Guere"
Courtesy of Rosalie Eppert

April 1917
"Our Eighth Movie Doll
Charlotte Walker"

May 1917
"Ninth Movie Paper Doll
Mary Miles Minter"
Courtesy of Rosalie Eppert

June 1917
"Our Tenth Movie Paper Doll
Pauline Frederick"
Courtesy of Rosalie Eppert

July 1917
"Charlie Chaplin
Our Eleventh Motion
Picture Paper Doll"
Courtesy of Rosalie Eppert

**August 1917
"Baby Marie Osborne
(Little Mary Sunshine)
Our Twelfth Movie Paper Doll"
Courtesy of Virginia Crossley**

**September 1917
"Our Thirteenth Movie Paper Doll
Mae Murray"
Courtesy of Rosalie Eppert**

**December 1917
"Our Fourteenth Movie Paper Doll
Madame Petrova"
Courtesy of Virginia Crossley**

**January 1918
"Mae Marsh
Our Fifteenth Movie Paper Doll"
Courtesy of Rosalie Eppert**

Life

This early *Life* magazine was published in New York From January 1883 to November 1936.

**October 1932
"Campaign Cut-Outs
For Conscientious Citizens"
(Franklin D. Roosevelt
and Herbert Hoover)**

McCall's

    McCall's celebrated its 100th anniversary in April 1976. The magazine was known as "The Queen of Fashion" in its early years and was founded by Belle and James McCall. The McCall's had started a pattern company, and the magazine was used to assist the sales of their patterns. Near the turn of the century, the magazine name was changed to *McCall's Magazine,* and in 1934, the title was changed simply to *McCall's.*

    Except for the June 1904 issue, the years before 1907 were not available for research. The following list contains all known paper dolls and paper toys that appeared in *McCall's.* The paper doll pages are pictured following the list.

1904
June - "The Little Girl and The Dog Cart" (paper toy)

1909
July - Sliced Puzzle cut-out
August - "Dolly Sunbonnet and Her New Clothes"
September - "Fun For the Little Folks" (puzzle picture)
October - "Miss Paper Doll and Her New Winter Clothes"
December - "Little Dolly Dolliver and Her Christmas Presents"

1910
January - "Dolly's Brother Dicky and Some of His Toys"
February - "Historical Picture Puzzle"
March - "Baby Dolliver and His Nurse"

April - "Easter Gifts For Little Folks" (paper toys)
May - "Dancing Round The May Pole" (paper toy)
June - "The Bride and Bridesmaid Paper Dolls"
July - Sliced Puzzle - "What Happened to Johnnie On the 4th Of July?"
September - "The Little Red School House and Two of the Pupils" (school and two children)
October - "Patty and Her Pets"

1911
January - No paper dolls, but there is an article and directions for a paper doll house
February - Paper furniture for a doll house
March - "The Mother of the Paper Doll Family"
April - "Aunt Dinah, The Colored Cook, Comes to Join the Paper Doll Family"
May - "Rosalind, The Eldest Daughter of the Paper Doll Family"
June - "Bobby and His Pet Dog Come To Join the

Paper Doll Family"
July - information not available
August - "Pony and Cart Cut-Out"
September - Snow White, Wicked Queen, Prince, Dwarfs (stand-up figures)
October - "The Giraffe, The Fairy Godmother, The Fawn and the Mice" (stand-up figures)
November - "Cinderella, The Glass Slipper and the Fairy Coach" (stand-up figures)
December - Page includes a Santa Claus, Christmas tree and candles, toys, etc.

1912
March - Page includes circus stand-up figures
October - "An Indian Wigwam For the Children" (paper toy)
November - "Nebuchadnezzar, The Captured Owl" (paper toy)
December - "Santa Claus's Christmas Chimney" (paper toy)

1913
January - "Brave Bobby and His Steed" (paper toy)
February - "The Animated Mock-Turtle" (paper toy)
March - "The Little Dutch Clock" (paper toy)
April - "Mother Hen and Her Little Family" (paper toy)
June - "A Wheelbarrow For Dolly's Garden" (paper toy)
July - "A Venetian Gondola and Gondolier" (paper toy)
August - "A Seesaw Cut-Out For the Children" (paper toy)
September - "Jinks' and Betty's Barrel Clown" (paper toy)
October - "Peter Pumpkin, Our Hallowe'en Visitor" (paper toy)
November - "The Turkey Who Wasn't Killed For Thanksgiving" (paper toy)
December - "A Jumping-Jack Cut-Out For the Children" (paper toy)

1914
January - "Robin Hood, The Bold Bandit" (paper toy)
February - "Our Betty As a Camp-Fire Girl"
March - "Jinks In His Boy-Scout Suit"
April - "A Whole Rabbit Family For Easter" (stand-up rabbits and rabbit hutch)
May - "The May Flower Garden" (paper toy)
June - "Betty's Archery Outfit" (paper toy)
July - "Betty In Her Canoe" (paper toy)
August - "The Two Hungry Dickey Birds" (paper toy)
September - "Simon, The Runaway Ape" (paper toy)

October - "The Hallowe'en Witch" (stand-up witch)
November - "Merry-Legs, The Mischievous Pony" (stand-up pony)
December - "Mike In Holiday Attire" (stand-up dog)

1915
January - "Running Bull, The Indian Boy" (stand-up toy)
February - "Betty's Valentine Mail-Box" (paper toy)
March - "Betty's New Friend" (papoose)
April - "The Little Dutch Windmill" (stand-up toy)
May - "The Mischievous Donkey" (paper toy)
June - "Our June Bride"
July - "An Automobile For the Whole Family" (stand-up toy)
August - "A Bird That Really Flies" (paper toy)
September - "Miss Dolly's Suit-Case" (paper toy)
October - "Alice In Wonderland"
November - "The White Rabbit"
December - "The Dodo" (stand-up figure)

1916
January - "The Dutchess"
February - "The Cheshire Cat" (stand-up figure)
March - "The Mad March Hare" (stand-up figure)
April - "The Cook With Her Kettle and Pepper Pot" (stand-up figure)
May - "The Hatter" (stand-up figure)
June - "The Executioner and the Gardener" (stand-up figures)
July - "The Queen of Hearts" (stand-up figures)
August - "Alice and Her Flamingo" (stand-up figures)
September - "The Knave of Hearts" (stand-up figure)
October - "The King of Hearts" (stand-up figure)
November - "The Mock-Turtle" (stand-up figure)
December - "The Gryphon" (stand-up figure)

1917
February - "The Jumble Picture" (cut and paste picture)
September - "Tweedledum and Tweedledee" (stand-up figures)

1918
January - "Jack and Peggy at the Zoo" (stand-up figures - the lion cage)
February - "Jack and Peggy at the Zoo" (stand-up figures - the monkey cage)
March - "Jack and Peggy at the Zoo" (stand-up figures - the hippopotamus cage)
June - "Silhouette Town" (stand-up buildings and figures)
July - information not available
December - "Dangling Dick" (paper toy)

1919

February - "Here Are Valentines" (valentines)
March - "The Chic Chicken"
April - "Easter Greetings" (poems)
May - "May Baskets" (paper toy)
July - "Pollykins Pudge Says 'Googlety-Goo' "
August - "Pollykins Pudge Says, 'How-Do-You-Do' "
September - "Pollykins Pudge Says, 'I'm Two Times Three' "
October - "Little Joy San, Comes From Japan."
November - "Katrinka's My Name; From Holland I Came"
December - Christmas cards

1920

January - No issue was found for this month. There is a possibility that a January issue was not printed as New York had a printers' strike at this time, and many magazines were affected by the strike.
February - "When Grandpa Was a Little Boy, and Grandmama Was Little, Too ..." (valentine)
March - "An Irish Colleen With Her Irish Pig"
April - "Here's Dear Old Molly-Cottontail, and Pa, and Buster Bunny"
May - "Baskets Gay For Flowers of May" (paper toy)
June - "The Circus Parade" (paper toy figures)
July - "Mr. Fish and Mrs. Crab Each Summer Smile With Glee ..."
August - "If You Would Ride In This Gay Com-Pa-Nee ..." (Merry-go-round paper toy)
September - "Swinging in the Hammock Is The Best Time of Summer Joys ... " (paper toy)
October - "In Eighteen Hundred Seventy, The Children Used To Play ..." (seesaw paper toy)
December - "I Sniffed a Jolly Woodsy Smell As I Came In Today" (Christmas tree ornaments)

1921

January - "Jack and Jill Have Come To Stay. They'll Play With You Most Any Day"
February - "Two Fancy Dress Parties, One After The Other ..."
March - "When Jack and Jill Dress As Easter Rabbits"
April - "In Springtime, Jack and Jill Agree, 'The Garden Is the Place For Me' "
May - "Maid and Gentleman in Waiting, Are Our Jack and Jill Today ... "
June - "Were You Ever Chased By a Mischievous Wave ..."
July - "Winsome Bet and Sue and Bill Are Off to Play With Jack and Jill ..."
August - "Elizabeth Discovers Teeny Town" (stand-up buildings and figures)
September - "More Buildings In Teeny Town" (stand-up buildings and figures)

October - "Train Time In Teeny Town" (stand-up buildings and train)
November - "Main Street, Teeny Town" (stand-up buildings)
December - "Another Corner of Teeny Town" (stand-up buildings, trees, etc.)

1922

January - "Going To Market and the Movies In Teeny Town" (stand-up buildings)
February - "The Big Show Comes to Teeny Town!" (stand-up figures of circus, big top, etc.)
March - "Alice's Adventures In Wonderland" (cut-out figures of Alice and friends)
April - "Splash!" (paper cut-out figures)
May - "Goldie Buttercup's Spring Dance" (paper cut-out figures)
June - "A Knight In June" (paper cut-out figures)
July - "The Flowers Big Parade" (paper cut-out figures)
August - "Strike Out For the Camp-Fire Trail!"
September - "Aladdin and the Wonderful Lamp" (paper cut-out figures)
October - "Treasure Island" (paper cut-out figures)
November - "Little Women" (paper cut-out figures)
December - "Jingle Bells! Santa Is Here!" (stand-up room and figures)

1923

January - "Mother Goose's New Broomstick" (paper toy)
February - "When Fairies Fly In Airplanes" (paper toy)
March - "Sir Oriole and Bandit Blue Jay Flyers" (paper toy)
April - "Robin Hood" (stand-up figures)
May - "Dappleton Farm" (stand-up house and figures of the Twinkle family)
June - "Where the Animals Live At Dappleton Farm" (stand-up buildings and figures)
July - "Dappleton Farm's Wagon House and Hay Barn" (stand-up buildings and wagons)
August - "A Brand New Barn At Dappleton Farm" (stand-up building)
September - "The Farm's Hennery and Windmill" (stand-up buildings)
October - "When Autumn Comes To Dappleton Farm" (stand-up scenes)
November - "Noah's Ark Shop" (stand-up figures)
December - "Santa and His Sack" (paper toy)

1924

January - "Slim and Sli, The Circus Clowns" (paper toy)
February - "Slim and Sli and Johnny Giraffe" (paper toy)
March - "Slim and Sli and the Baby Elephant"

(paper toy)

April - "Sunshine Cottage, the Children's Happi-House" (cottage with cut-out figures)

May - "The Living Room of Sunshine Cottage" (room with cut-out figures)

June - "The Dining Room of Sunshine Cottage" (room with cut-out figures)

July - "The Bedroom of Sunshine Cottage" (room with cut-out figures)

August - "The Nursery of Sunshine Cottage" (room with cut-out figures)

September - "The Kitchen of Sunshine Cottage" (room with cut-out figures)

October - "Nipper, The Snap-Shooter, Goes Gunning In The Rockies" (stand-up figures)

November - "Nipper Goes Snap-Shooting In The Arctic" (stand-up figures)

December - "Santa's Magic Snowball" (paper toys and tree ornaments)

1925

January - "Nipper Goes Snap-Shooting In Africa" (stand-up)

February - "Nipper Goes Snap-Shooting In India" (stand-up figures)

March - "Nipper Goes Snap-Shooting In Australia" (stand-up figures)

April - "Nipper In Italy" (stand-up figures)

May - "Nipper Takes His Camera To the Circus" (stand-up figures)

June - "Martha and George Washington"

July - "John Adams and Abigail, His Wife"

August - "The Madisons and Their Family Carriage" (stand-up figures)

September - "Mrs. McCall and Little Betty"

October - "Master McCall and Sister Nell"

November - "Sister Nell Goes To a Party"

December - "Betty Goes Christmas Shopping"

1926

January - "The Twins Make a New Year Call"

March - "Baby McCall Goes For a Ride"

April - "Two Jolly Playmates Romp In The Park"

May - "A Boudoir Doll"

June - "Doll Boudoir Set" (stand-up furniture)

July - "Doll Boudoir Set" (stand-up furniture)

The longest series of paper dolls is the "Betsy McCall" series. They began in May 1951 and ran for more than 30 years. The paper dolls are listed here but not pictured.*

*Betsy McCall is copyrighted by the McCall Publishing Co.

The Betsy McCall Paper Doll Series
1951

May - "Introducing Betsy McCall"

June - "Betsy McCall Goes to the Beach"

July - "Betsy McCall Goes to the Country"

August - "Betsy McCall Goes Shopping"

September - "Betsy McCall Goes To School"

October - "Here's Betsy McCall"

November - "Betsy McCall Has a Wonderful Thanksgiving"

December - "Betsy McCall Has a Merry Christmas"

1952

January - "Betsy McCall Goes To a Wedding"

February - "Betsy McCall Gets a Valentine"

March - "Betsy McCall Speaks Her Piece"

April - "Betsy McCall Goes To An Easter Egg Hunt"

May - "Betsy McCall Goes On a Picnic"

June - "Nosy Gives Betsy McCall A Bath"

July - "Betsy McCall Goes To The Beach"

August - "Betsy and Nosy Go To The Circus"

September - "Betsy McCall Gets a Doll"

October - "Betsy McCall Meets A Witch"

November - "Betsy McCall Goes Dancing"

December - "Betsy McCall Writes To Santa Claus"

1953

January - "Betsy McCall Finds A Surprise"

February - "Betsy McCall and The Cherry Pie"

March - "Betsy McCall Plays A Joke"

April - "Put The Dress on Betsy"

May - "Betsy McCall Is Locked Out"

June - "Betsy McCall Meets A Sea Monster"

July - "Betsy McCall Has A Parade"

August - "Betsy McCall Saves For A Bond"

September - "Betsy McCall Has Her Picture Taken"

October - "Betsy McCall's Halloween"

November - "Betsy McCall Has A Half-Birthday"

December - "Betsy McCall Waits Up For Santa"

1954

January - "Betsy McCall Has A Tea Party"

February - "Betsy McCall Ices A Cake"

March - "Betsy McCall Plays The Piano"

April - "Betsy McCall Rolls Easter Eggs"

May - "Betsy McCall Loses Her Bow"

June - "Betsy McCall Goes To The Country"

July - "Betsy McCall's Flower Garden"

August - "Betsy McCall Plays School"

September - "Betsy McCall Is Topsy-Turvy"

October - "Betsy McCall and Her New Book"

November - "Help Betsy McCall Find Her Doll"

November - "Betsy McCall Says, 'To Little Girls Who Plan To Grow - Your Dresses Must Not Shrink' " (Black and white ad by American Viscose Corporation. The ad includes a paper doll of Betsy McCall and three outfits.)

December - "Betsy McCall Trims The Tree"

1955

January - "Betsy McCall Starts A New Year"

February - "Betsy McCall's Valentine Surprise"

March - "Betsy McCall Plays A Game"

April - "Betsy McCall Decorates An Egg"
May - "Betsy McCall Makes A Starfish"
June - "Betsy McCall Has A Beach Picnic"
July - "Betsy McCall Goes Western"
August - "Betsy McCall Goes To A Birthday Party" (two pages)
September - "A Story For Betsy McCall"
October - "Betsy McCall Meets a Witch"
November - "Betsy McCall Makes A Wish"
December - "Betsy McCall's Christmas Surprise"

1956

January - "Betsy McCall Says Thank You" (thank you letters, not paper dolls)
February - "Betsy McCall Does A Good Turn"
March - "Betsy McCall Goes To The Flower Show"
April - "Betsy McCall Helps Her Cousin Barbara"
May - "Betsy McCall Has a Circus Birthday Party"
June - "Betsy McCall Takes A Picture of Nosy"
July - "Betsy McCall Makes A Hollyhock Doll" (not a paper doll page)
August - "Betsy McCall Plays a Game"
September - "Betsy McCall Makes A Necklace"
October - "Betsy McCall Plants a Rose Garden"
November - "Betsy McCall's Thanksgiving Day"
December - "Betsy McCall On Christmas Eve"

1957

January - "Betsy McCall Makes Her Own Puppets" (puppets of Goldilocks and the three bears)
February - "Betsy McCall On Valentine's Day"
March - "Betsy McCall Tells Cousin Linda A Story"
April - "Betsy McCall Gets a New Pet"
May - "Betsy McCall Visits Her Aunt Helen"
June - "Betsy McCall Plays Tick-Tack-Toe"
July - "Betsy McCall's Tea Party" (a cut-out tea set but no paper dolls)
August - "Betsy McCall Finds A Four-Leaf Clover"
September - "Betsy McCall Learns How To Sew"
October - "Betsy McCall Goes To The Zoo"
November - "Betsy McCall Meets Captain Kangaroo"
December - "Betsy McCall Gives Nosy A Christmas Present"

1958

January - "Betsy McCall Makes A Calendar" (not a paper doll page)
February - "Betsy McCall Has A Valentine Picnic"
March - "Betsy McCall On St. Patrick's Day"
April - "Betsy McCall Looks For Easter Eggs"
May - "Betsy McCall Goes To The Children's Zoo"
June - "Betsy McCall Visits A Friend"
July - "Betsy McCall Has A Fourth of July Party"
August - "Betsy McCall" ("I am Betsy McCall. See my three new dresses.")
September - "Betsy McCall Goes To School"
October - "Betsy McCall" ("Eating out together is always fun ... ")
November - "Betsy McCall's Cousin Linda Goes To Romper Room"
November - "A Letter To Santa From Betsy McCall" (not a paper doll page)
December - "Betsy McCall" (paper dolls and Christmas poems)

1959

January - "Betsy McCall" (The new year comes, the old year goes ...)
February - "Betsy McCall" (Hearts are red and skies are blue ...)
March - "Betsy McCall Writes Grandma A Letter"
April - "Betsy McCall Makes a Rainy-Day Surprise!"
May - "Betsy McCall Flies A Kite!"
June - "Betsy McCall Goes To West Point"
July - "Betsy McCall Visits The White House"
August - "Betsy McCall Goes To A Dolls' Fashion Show"
September - "Betsy McCall Visits The United Nations"
October - "Betsy McCall Visits Miss Frances' Ding Dong School"
November - "Betsy McCall Visits Roy Rogers' Ranch"
December - "Betsy McCall's Scrambled Christmas List" (not a paper doll page)

1960

January - "Betsy McCall Visits Leonard Bernstein"
February - "Betsy McCall Visits Colonial Williamsburg"
March - "Two New Betsy McCall Dresses" (two outfits but no paper doll)
April - "Betsy McCall Visits Her Grandmother"
May - "Betsy McCall Takes A Trip Down The Mississippi"
June - "Betsy McCall Vists The Festival Of Roses"
July - Betsy McCall Takes A Trip On The California Zephyr"
August - "Betsy McCall Visits Pollyanna"
September - "Betsy McCall Visits a County Fair"
October - "Betsy McCall Goes To The Ballet"
November - "Betsy McCall Visits Radio City"
December - "Betsy McCall Visits Grandma For Christmas"

1961

January - "Betsy McCall Makes a 1961 Calendar" (not a paper doll page)
February - "Betsy McCall Goes To The Westminster Dog Show"
March - "Betsy McCall Visits McCall's"
May - "Betsy McCall and Linda Go To The Circus"
June - "Betsy McCall Plants a Garden"
July - "Betsy McCall Visits Cape Cod"

From August to December there are Betsy McCall pages but no paper dolls.

1962

January - "Betsy McCall Makes a 1962 Calendar" (not a paper doll page)
February - "Betsy McCall Goes Skating"
March - "Betsy McCall Goes To Dancing School"
April - "Betsy McCall Gets A New Piano"
May - "Betsy McCall Plants a Garden"
June - "Betsy McCall Goes To A Wedding"
July - "Betsy McCall Goes To The Seashore"
August - "Betsy McCall Goes To Fairy-Tale Land"
September - "Betsy McCall and the Bluebirds"
October - "Betsy McCall At The Pet Show"
November - "Betsy McCall's Party Month"
December - "Betsy McCall's Christmas Greetings"

1963

January - "Betsy McCall's Calendar For 1963" (not a paper doll page)
February - "Betsy McCall's Trip To New York"
March - "Betsy, Linda and the Easter Rabbit"
April - "Betsy McCall Visits Greenfield Village"
May - "Betsy McCall Visits 'Oliver!' "
June - "Betsy McCall's Dog, Nosey, Becomes a Father"
July* - "Betsy McCall Goes Camping"
August - "Betsy McCall Writes From Italy"
September - "Betsy McCall Adopts A Kitten"
October - "Betsy McCall and the UN Fashion Show"
November - "Betsy McCall Gives a Sing-a-Long Party"
December - "Christmas Morning At Betsy McCall's"

(The July 1963 issue of McCall's had a nice article titled, "A Doll's Eye View Of History" with four pages of pictures showing antique paper dolls.)

1964

January - "The Betsy McCall Calendar For 1964" (not a paper doll page)
February - "Betsy McCall Writes From The Bahamas"
March - "Betsy McCall At The Egg-Rolling"
April - "Betsy McCall At The World's Fair"
May - "Betsy McCall and the Baby Robin"
June - "Betsy McCall and the Wedding Gown"
July - "Betsy McCall Writes From Camp"
August - "Betsy McCall Goes Dog-Walking"
September - "Betsy McCall: Traffic Monitor"
October - "Betsy Meets The New Betsy McCall Doll"
November - "Betsy McCall's School Prepares For Thanksgiving"
December - "Betsy McCall's Wonderful Christmas"

1965

January - "Betsy McCall Calendar For 1965" (not a paper doll page)
February - "Betsy McCall's Big Surprise"
March - "Betsy McCall, Junior Girl Scout"
April - "Betsy McCall Writes From Bermuda"
May - "Betsy McCall At The Flower Show"
June - "Betsy McCall Goes To A Wedding"
July - "Betsy McCall Goes To a Country Auction"
August - "Betsy McCall Writes A Letter From Camp"
September - "Betsy McCall and the Big News"
October - "Betsy McCall and the FUNICEF"
November - "Betsy McCall Gives a Dolls' Tea Party"
December - "Betsy's Christmas At Great-Grandma McCall's"

1966

January - "Betsy McCall Calendar For 1966" (not a paper doll page)
February - "Betsy McCall Becomes a Sister"
March - "Betsy, Linda and the First Robin"
April - "Betsy McCall's Easter Tree"
May - "Betsy McCall Writes From Kentucky"
June - "Betsy McCall Finds A Treasure"
August - "Betsy McCall Goes To A Beach Party"
September - "Betsy McCall's Trailer Trip To Yellowstone"
October - "Betsy McCall Bakes Cookies For Unicef"
November - "Daddy McCall Builds a Dollhouse For Betsy"
December - "Christmas At Betsy McCall's"

1967

January - "Betsy McCall Calendar For 1967" (not a paper doll page)
February - "Betsy McCall, Sculptress"
March - "Easter At Grandma McCall's"
April - "Betsy McCall Goes To the Planetarium"
May - "Betsy McCall and the Maypole Dance"
July - "Betsy McCall and the Myna"
August - "Besty McCall Writes From Expo 67"
October - "Betsy McCall and the Unicef Play"
December - "Betsy McCall Writes 'Dear Santa' "

1968

March - "Haircuts For the McCall Twins"
April - "Betsy McCall's April Fool"
August - "Betsy McCall Writes From 'Meh-He-Ko' "
September - "Betsy McCall's Adventure In The Rain"
October - "Betsy Meets A Friend Of Unicef"

1969

February - "Betsy Gives A Valentine Party"
June - "Betsy's Farm Weekend"
July - "Betsy Writes From Holland"

September - "Betsy Writes From Switzerland"
October - "Betsy's School Has An Eat-In For Unicef"
November - "Betsy Has a Thanksgiving Surprise"
December - "Betsy and the Birds' Christmas Carol"

1970

January - "Betsy McCall's Calendar For 1970" (not a paper doll page)
May - "Betsy Celebrates Mother's Day - Sort Of"
June - "Daddy Helps Betsy Plan A Trip"
July - "Betsy Writes A Letter From France"
August - "The Betsy McCall Cookbook" (nine pages, one page is a paper doll page)
September - "The Twins Go To Play School"
October - "Adventures On A Windy Day"
November - "Open House At Betsy's School"
December - "Betsy McCall - My Embroidery Book" (four pages, one is a paper doll page)

1971

January - "Betsy McCall Calendar" (for 1971, not a paper doll page)

Beginning with the February 1971 issue, the McCall's magazines are of a smaller size.

February - "Betsy Writes From Colonial Williamsburg"
March - "Betsy's Sunday At the Metropolitan Museum of Art"
April - "Betsy McCall - Circus Clown For A Day (The Greatest Show On Earth)"
June - "Betsy McCall Tries Five New Hairdos"
August - "Betsy McCall Writes From Spain"
September - "Betsy McCall's Town Fights Pollution"
October - "Betsy McCall At the Unicefair"
December - "Betsy McCall Is A Cookie Cutter"

1972

January - "Betsy McCall's Calendar For 1972" (not a paper doll)
February - "Betsy McCall Visits The Joffrey Ballet"
April - "Betsy McCall Visits The Plaza"
May - "Betsy McCall Makes An Apple Doll"
June - "Betsy McCall's Daddy Is A Hero"
August - "Betsy McCall Writes From Portugal"
September - "Betsy McCall Learns Symbol Talk"
October - "Betsy McCall's Town Bakes For Unicef"
November - "Big Doll Robbery At Betsy McCall's!"
December - "Betsy McCall Celebrates Lucia Day"

1973

January - "Betsy McCall's Calendar For 1973" (not a paper doll page)
February - "Betsy McCall Writes From The French West Indies"
March - "Easter Eggcitement At Betsy McCall's

School"
June - "The Haunted House in Betsy McCall's Town"
August - "Betsy McCall Visits The Pennsylvania Dutch"
September - "Betsy McCall Finds A Place In The Woods"
October - "Betsy McCall Becomes a Foster Parent"
November - "Merry November to You From All of Us"
December - "Betsy McCall Writes From Christmas World"

1974

April - "Betsy McCall's Class Visits Washington"
August - "Betsy McCall Writes From Sanibel Island"

1975

January - "Betsy McCall's Calendar For 1975" (not a paper doll page)
September - "Betsy and the Spelling Bee"
November - "Betsy Learns To Ride"

1976

March - "Betsy McCall: Having Fun With Seeds"
April - "Growing Up With Betsy McCall"
September - "Betsy Visits Grandma's House"

1977

February - "Betsy McCall Is Adopted (By A Cat)!"
September - "Betsy McCall's Family Album"
December - "Betsy McCall Gives A Puppet Show"

1978

February - "Betsy McCall Writes From Hawaii"
March - "Betsy McCall Turns Magician"
April - "Betsy McCall Decorates Mother's Sewing Box"
August - "Betsy McCall Takes A Canoe Trip" (no outfits for the dolls)
November - "Betsy McCall Goes Flying"
December - "Betsy McCall's Prettiest Christmas"

1979

March - "Betsy McCall Finds a Friend"
September - "Betsy McCall Visits a Cider Mill"
December - "Betsy McCall Trims A Tree For Her Friends"

1980

April - "Betsy McCall Learns To Skate"

1981

September - "Betsy McCall Gets The Picture"

1982

December - "Betsy McCall's Most Christmasy

Christmas"

1984
December - "Betsy McCall's Best Present"

1986
April, May, July and October had Betsy McCall puzzle and activity pages, but no paper dolls.

A 16-page Betsy McCall magazine was introduced in the September 1988 issue of McCall's, and a second one appeared in the December issue. Paper dolls were not included in either one.

**August 1909
Courtesy of Virginia Crossley**

**October 1909
Courtesy of Virginia Crossley**

**December 1909
From the Jane Sugg Collection**

**January 1910
From the Jane Sugg Collection**

March 1910
From the Jane Sugg Collection

June 1910
Courtesy of Virginia Crossley

October 1910
"Patty and Her Pets" was not
available to photograph

March 1911
Courtesy of Virginia Crossley

April 1911
Courtesy of Virginia Crossley

May 1911
Courtesy of Virginia Crossley

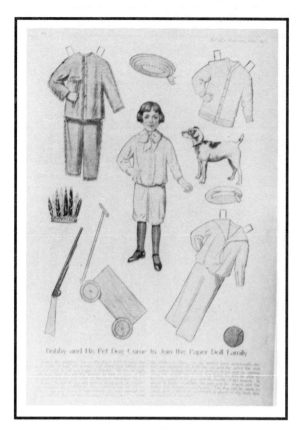

June 1911
Courtesy of Virginia Crossley

August 1911

February 1914
Courtesy of Virginia Crossley

March 1914
Courtesy of Virginia Crossley

June 1915
Courtesy of Virginia Crossley

October 1915
Courtesy of Rosalie Eppert

November 1915
Courtesy of Rosalie Eppert

January 1916
Courtesy of Virginia Crossley

March 1919
Courtesy of Virginia Crossley

July 1919
From the Jane Sugg Collection

August 1919

September 1919

October 1919
Courtesy of Virginia Crossley

November 1919

March 1920
Courtesy of Virginia Crossley

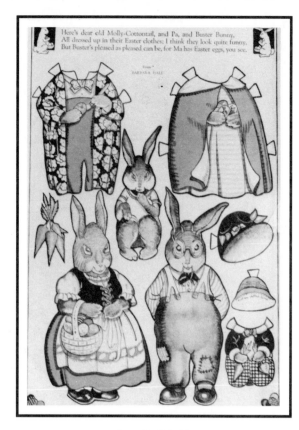

April 1920
Courtesy of Virginia Crossley

July 1920
Courtesy of Rosalie Eppert

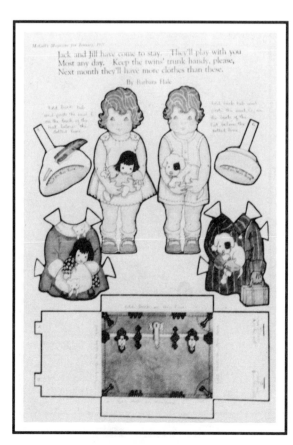

January 1921
Courtesy of Virginia Crossley

February 1921
Courtesy of Virginia Crossley

March 1921

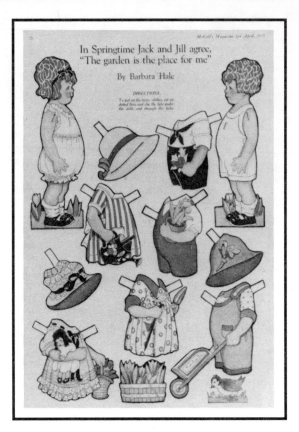

April 1921

May 1921

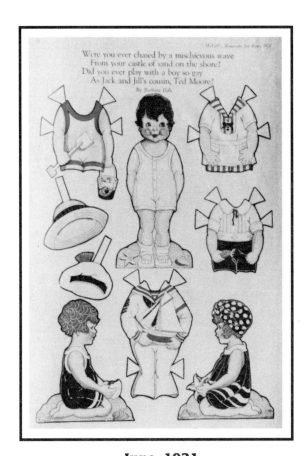

June 1921

All paper doll pages pictured on this page are courtesy of Virginia Crossley

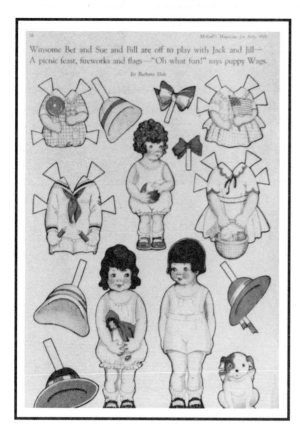

July 1921
Courtesy of Virginia Crossley

August 1922

June 1925
Courtesy of Virginia Crossley

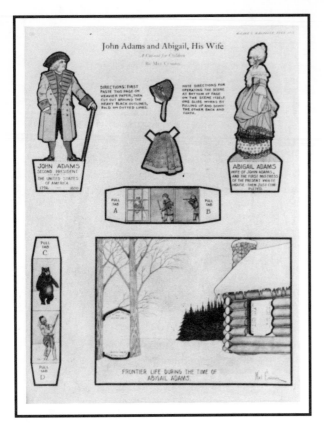

July 1925

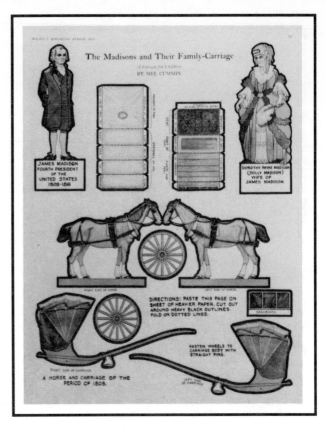

August 1925
Courtesy of Rosalie Eppert

September 1925

October 1925
Courtesy of Virginia Crossley

November 1925

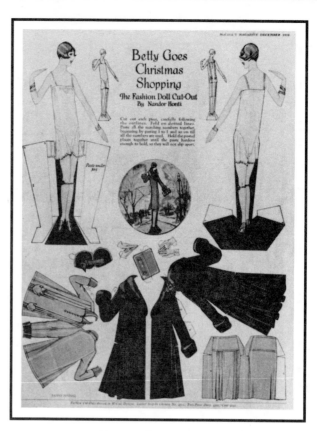

December 1925

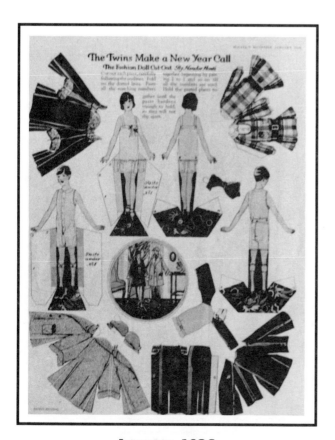

January 1926

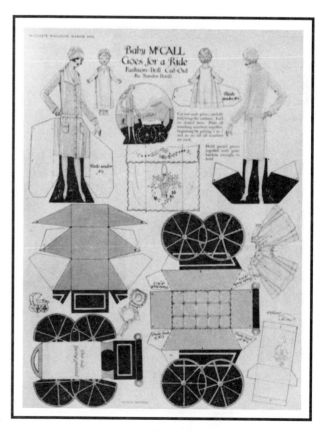

March 1926

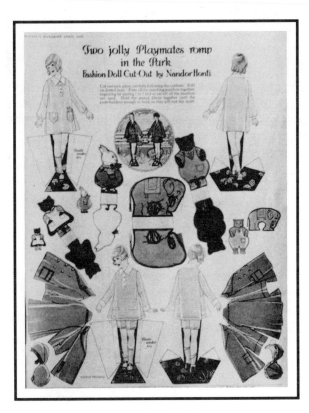

April 1926

May 1926

McCall's Needlework

Fall 1924
"Little Molly McCall and
Her Pets, Blinky and Winx"
Courtesy of Shirley Hedge

Winter 1924/1925
"Jolly Baby Jean and
Her French Nurse, Celeste"
Courtesy of Barbara Faber

The Metropolitan

The Metropolitan was published by the Metropolitan Life Insurance Company of New York. Although the magazines had volume numbers, the magazine itself was not dated. From references inside the magazine, it has been determined the issues that contained paper dolls were published from 1924 to 1926. The paper doll pages are not signed but are believed to be by the same artists who drew the paper doll series in *Good Housekeeping* from October 1923 to March 1926. Following the paper doll series were four other children's pages (in 1926 and 1927) featuring a paper toy of a doll which could be activated to move and do exercises to show children how to keep healthy. (Each page is titled *Mother Metropolitan's Healthy Boys and Girls.*)

A special thank you to Mr. James Mann, Archivist of the Metropolitan Life Insurance Co. who sent me the information and material for the pictures, and to Barbara Faber who owns the little farmer boy from Vol. 30, #1.

Volume 29, #10 circa 1924
Courtesy of James Mann

Volume 29, #11 circa 1924/1925
Courtesy of James Mann

Volume 29, #12 circa 1925/1926
Courtesy of James Mann

Volume 30, #1 circa 1926
Courtesy of Barbara Faber

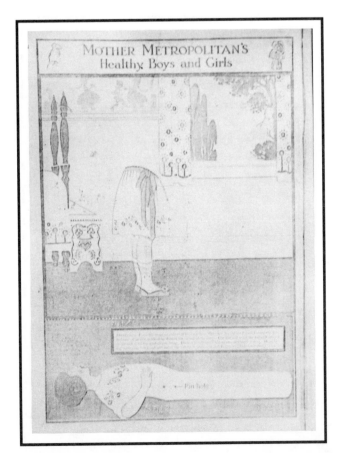

Volume 30, #2 circa 1926
(Doll's name is "Peggy")
Courtesy of James Mann

Volume 30, #3 circa 1927
(Doll's name is "Billy")
Courtesy of James Mann

Volume 30, #4 circa 1927
(Doll's name is "Sally")
Courtesy of James Mann

Volume 30, #5 circa 1927
(Doll's name is "Willie")
Courtesy of James Mann

Movie Magazine

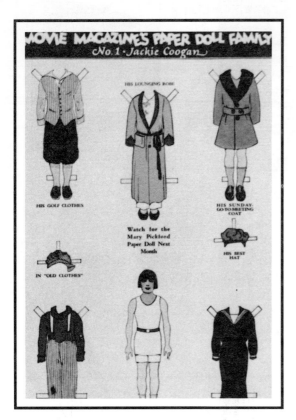

**December 1925
"Movie Magazine's Paper Doll Family
No. 1 - Jackie Coogan"
Courtesy of Emma Terry**

Other paper dolls are known to be in this series but were not available.

Movies

**January 1940
"Cut Out and Dress Deanna" (Durbin)
Courtesy of Emma Terry**

"Cut Out and Dress Virginia" (Weidler)
Date not verified
Courtesy of Carol Carey

March 1940
"Cut Out and
Dress Larry" (Simms)
Courtesy of Carol Carey

"Cut Out and Dress Gloria Jean"
Date not verified
Courtesy of Emma Terry

Normal Instructor, Primary Plans, The Instructor

In May of 1981, two magazines, *The Teacher* and *The Instructor,* combined to form *Instructor and Teacher. The Instructor* got its roots in November 1891 when the magazine *Normal Instructor* was started in Dansville, New York by Frederick A. Owen. In 1902, *Teacher's World* was bought and merged with *Normal Instructor.* A second magazine was started by the F. A. Owen Publishing Co. in 1903 and was called *Primary Plans.* In 1914, the company's two magazines combined and were called *Normal Instructor and Primary Plans.* (In November 1919, the company also began publishing *Junior Instructor* which is covered elsewhere in this book.) In 1931, *Normal Instructor and Primary Plans* was shortened to *The Instructor* and continued to 1981 when it joined with *The Teacher* which had entirely different roots as shown below.

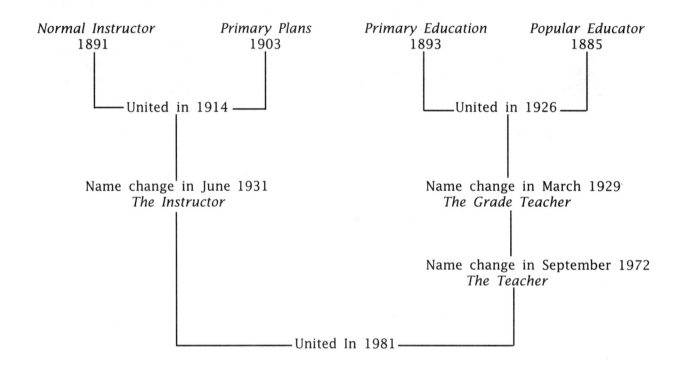

Normal Instructor
1891

Primary Plans
1903

United in 1914

Name change in June 1931
The Instructor

Primary Education
1893

Popular Educator
1885

United in 1926

Name change in March 1929
The Grade Teacher

Name change in September 1972
The Teacher

United In 1981

Old issues of *Normal Instructor* were not easily found and those that were did not contain paper dolls. Occasionally some stand-up paper toys were found. No issues of *Primary Plans* before March 1911 were ever found for this research. Of about 20 issues of *Primary Plans* that were found, only two contained paper dolls which are pictured here.

**September 1913
"Primary Plans"
(a partial page)**

**March 1911
"Primary
Plans"**

The early issues of the combined *Normal Instructor and Primary Plans* were equally hard to find, but one paper doll in June 1914 was found and is pictured. The years from 1919 to June 1931 were extensively researched, and although there were many paper toys, only one paper doll was issued, and this coincided with a paper doll published the same month in *Junior Instructor.* The month was October 1920, and both paper dolls were the same but had different titles. "Judy, A Paper Doll For A Doll House" appeared in *Normal Instructor and Primary Plans,* and in *Junior Instructor* the page was called "Judy Herself." The *Junior Instructor* continued with a series of "Judy" paper dolls but *Normal Instructor and Primary Plans* did not.

**June 1914
"Mother Goose Paper Dolls"
Courtesy of Marlene Brenner**

**October 1920
"Judy - A Paper Doll
For A Doll House"
Courtesy of Carol Kennedy**

**September 1931
"Paper Dolls - Children of
the United States"
Courtesy of Rosalie Eppert**

After June 1931 when *Normal Instructor and Primary Plans* shortened its title to *The Instructor*, some paper doll pages as well as some nice stand-up pages were included in several issues. *The Instructor* was checked from 1931 through 1940.

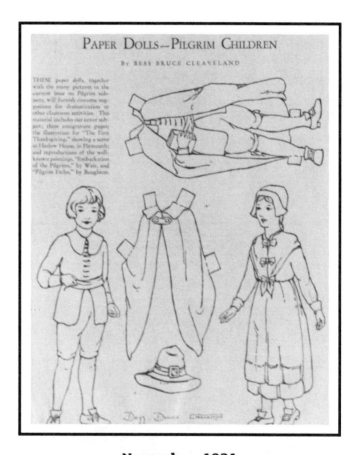

**November 1931
"Paper Dolls - Pilgrim Children"
Courtesy of Rosalie Eppert**

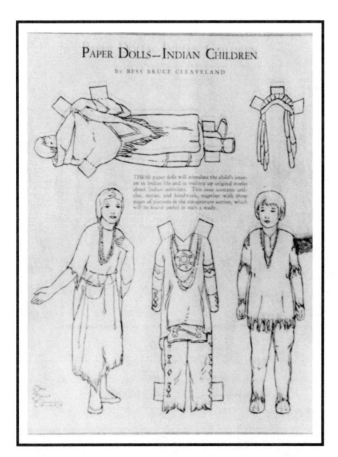

**October 1931
"Paper Dolls - Indian Children"
Courtesy of Rosalie Eppert**

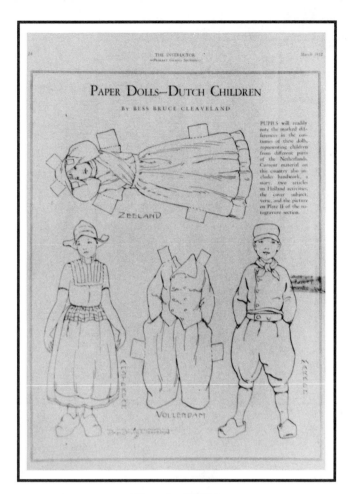

March 1932
"Paper Dolls - Dutch Children"
Courtesy of Rosalie Eppert

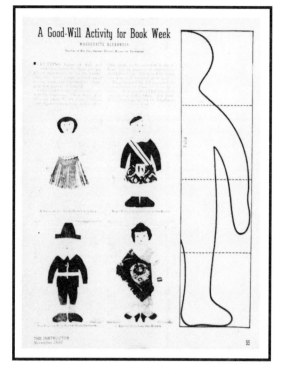

November 1935
This page shows a pattern for a paper doll with instructions for designing different outfits for the doll.

January 1937
"Dolls From Mother Goose Land"

February 1937
"Dolls From Mother Goose Land"

December 1936
"A Doll Of Long Ago"
This page pictures an antique paper doll and her six costumes. Also included is a line drawing of the same doll and one outfit.

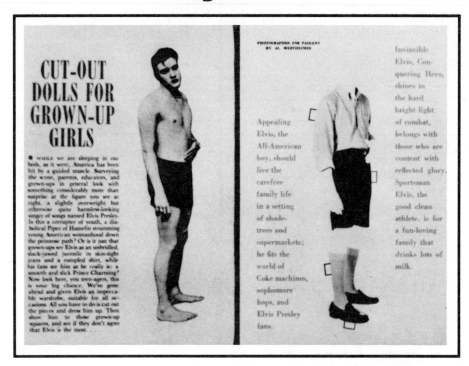

CUT-OUT DOLLS FOR GROWN-UP GIRLS

PHOTOGRAPHED FOR PAGEANT BY AL WERTHEIMER

While we are sleeping in our beds, as it were, America has been hit by a guided muscle. Surveying the scene, parents, educators, and grown-ups in general look with something considerably more than surprise at the figure you see at right, a slightly overweight but otherwise quite harmless-looking singer of songs named Elvis Presley. Is this a corrupter of youth, a diabolical Piper of Hamelin strumming young American womanhood down the primrose path? Or is it just that grown-ups see Elvis as an unbridled, slack-jawed juvenile in skin-tight jeans and a rumpled shirt, while his fans see him as he really is: a smooth and slick Prince Charming? Now look here, you teen-agers, this is your big chance. We've gone ahead and given Elvis an impeccable wardrobe, suitable for all occasions. All you have to do is cut out the pieces and dress him up. Then show him to those grown-up squares, and see if they don't agree that Elvis is the most.

Appealing Elvis, the All-American boy, should live the carefree family life in a setting of shade-trees and supermarkets; he fits the world of Coke machines, sophomore hops, and Elvis Presley fans.

Invincible Elvis, Conquering Hero, shines in the hard bright light of combat, belongs with those who are content with reflected glory. Sportsman Elvis, the good clean athlete, is for a fun-loving family that drinks lots of milk.

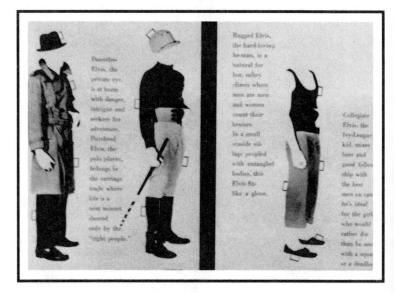

Dauntless Elvis, the private eye, is at home with danger, intrigue and seeks for adventure. Purebred Elvis, the polo player, belongs to the carriage trade where life is a neat minuet danced only by the "right people."

Rugged Elvis, the hard-loving he-man, is a natural for hot, sultry climes where men are men and women count their bruises. In a small seaside village peopled with entangled bodies, this Elvis fits like a glove.

Collegiate Elvis, the Ivy-League kid, mixes beer and good fellowship with the best men on campus; he's ideal for the girl who would rather die than be seen with a square or a deadhead.

"Cut-Out Dolls For Grown-Up Girls" (Elvis Presley) 1950's (Date not verified) Courtesy of Emma Terry

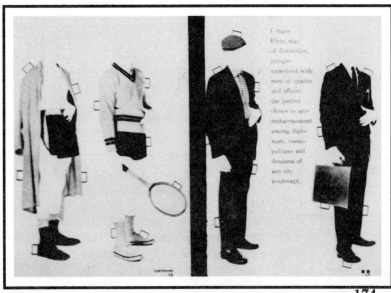

Urbane Elvis, man of distinction, mingles unnoticed with men of quality and affairs; the perfect choice to save embarrassment among diplomats, cosmopolites and denizens of any city boulevard.

Parents' Magazine

Parents' Magazine began in 1926. The magazine was known as *Children, The Parents' Magazine* from 1926 to July 1929.

The paper doll pages shown appeared in shades of black/white/grey.

August 1939
"Fall Washables Cut Out For School

Not Shown: **June 1971**
"Sew A Summer Wardrobe"
(two pages in black/white/ green)

February 1940
Patsy Parent Starts The New Year in Rayon"

People's Popular Monthly

People's Popular Monthly (The Homecraft Magazine) was published in Des Moines, Iowa. The magazine started in 1896 and ran until 1931. The known paper dolls are pictured. They are of limited color.

June 1928 Cover of
People's Popular Monthly

January 1928
"Tom, The Piper's Son
and Miss Moffit"
Courtesy of Shirley Hedge

February 1928
"This Is Mother Goose's
Little Polly Flinders"
Courtesy of Shirley Hedge

April 1928
"This is Lucy Locket
With Her Easter Clothes"
Courtesy of Shirley Hedge

June 1928
"Tommy Snooks and Bessie Brooks"
Courtesy of Helen Johnson

July 1928
"Here Are The Queen Of
Hearts and Old King Cole ..."
Courtesy of Helen Johnson

September 1928
"Mother Goose Herself"
Courtesy of Shirley Hedge

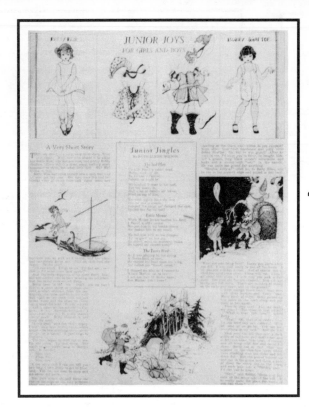

**October 1928
"Betty Blue, Bobby Shaftoe"
Courtesy of Shirley Hedge**

Pictorial Review

Pictorial Review was published in New York by the Pictorial Review Company from 1899 to 1939. *The Delineator* merged with *Pictorial Review* in 1937.

The following list contains all known paper dolls and paper toys that appeared in *Pictorial Review.* The paper dolls are pictured following the list.

1909
April - "Ted E. Bear Goes A-Hunting"
May - "Ted E. Bear Goes A-Hunting"
June - "The Adventures of Ted The Hunter In Africa"
September - "The Adventures of Ted The Hunter In Africa"
October - "The Adventures of Ted The Hunter In Africa"
November - "The Sir John Tenniel Alice In Wonderland Paper Cut-Out"
December - "The Sir John Tenniel Alice In Wonderland Paper Cut-Out - No. 2"

1910
January - "The Sir John Tenniel Alice In Wonderland Paper Cut-Out - No. 3"
February - "The Sir John Tenniel Alice In Wonderland Paper Cut-Out - No. 4"

1913
March - "Dolly Dingle of Dingle Dell"
April - "Billie Bumps of Dingle Dell"
May - "Kitty-Cutie of Dingle Dell"
June - "Frisky-Fido of Dingle Dell"
October - "Goldilocks and the Three Bears" (cut-out story play for "Pictorial Review Theater")

**November 1917
Cover of *Pictorial Review***

December - "Pictorial Review Theater Cut-Out Play No. II - The Night Before Christmas"

1914

January - "Pictorial Review Theater Cut-Out Play No. III - Little Red Riding Hood"
February - "Pictorial Review Theater Cut-Out Play No. IV - Cinderella"
March - "Hansel and Gretel" (stand-up figures)
April - "Snow White and the Seven Dwarfs" (stand-up figures)
May - "Old Mother Hulda" (stand-up figures)
December - "A Page of Christmas Poster Stamps" (to cut out and paste on Christmas packages)

1916

January - "Puss In Boots" (stand-up figures)
February - "Wig-Wag Cut-Outs For Valentine's Day" (cut-out figures for valentines)
March - "Dolly Dingle of Dingle Dell"
April - "Billie Bumps of Dingle Dell"
May - "Dolly Dingle As Queen Of The May"
June - "Dolly Dingle's Baby Brother"
July - "Dolly Dingle's Little Sister Toodles"
August - "Dolly Dingle On The Farm"
September - "Sammy Snooks and His Pets"
October - "Dolly Dingle's Hallowe'en"
November - "The Mousie Bride"
December - "Dolly Dingle's Christmas Party" (two pages)

1917

"Dolly Dingle's Trip Around The World"
January - "In The Land of the Cherry Blossom"
February - "Dolly Visits The Home Of The Mandarins"
March - "Dolly Visits The Palace Of The Grand Moguls"
April - "Dolly Visits The Land Of The Pharaohs"
May - "This Month Your Little Playmate Visits Sunny Italy"
June - "This Month Dolly Picks Edelweiss In The Tyrol"
July - "This Month Dolly Visits The Spanish Dons"
August - "Dolly Doing Her Bit 'Somewhere In France' "
September - "Dolly Picks Tulips By The Zuider Zee"
October - "This Month Dolly Visits The Land O' The Heather"
November - "This Month Dolly Kisses The Blarney Stone"
December - "Dolly Dingle Back Home Again For A Good American Christmas" (two pages)

1918

January - "Dolly Dingle Joins The Red Cross"
February - "Dolly Dingle's Patriotic Party"

March - "Dolly Dingle's Army and Navy Canteen"
April - "Dolly Dingle and Her War Garden"
May - "Dolly Dingle Adopts A War Orphan"
June - "Dolly Dingle Has a June Wedding"
July - "Introducing Dolly Dingle's Father"
August - "Introducing Dolly Dingle's Mother"
September - "Dolly Dingle Gives A Harvest Party"
October - "Dolly Dingle Celebrates Hallowe'en"
November - "Dolly Dingle Gives A Thanksgiving Dinner"
December - "Dolly Dingle Celebrates Her Christmas In True War-Time Style" (two pages)
December - "Dolly Dingle's War-Time Christmas Greetings" (Christmas cards)

1919

January - "Dolly Dingle's War Savings Stamp Party" (no outfits for the dolls)
January - "Dolly Dingle's New-Year Cards" (greeting cards)
February - "Dolly Dingle's Washington's Birthday Party" (no outfits for the dolls)
March - "Dolly Dingle's Welcome-Home Party"
April - "Dolly Dingle's Cut-Out Easter Cards" (Easter cards)
May - "A New Series of Dolly Dingle Cut-Outs"
June - "Bobby Blake In His New Sunday Suit"
July - "Dolly Dingle Is A Flower-Girl At Auntie's Wedding"
August - "Dolly Dingle's Cousin Gladys Gives A Fancy Dress Party"
September - "Dolly Dingle's Friend Betsy"
October - "Billy Bumps Goes To School"
October - "Dolly Dingle's Birthday Cards For All The Family"
November - "Dolly Dingle's Cousin Lucile"

1920

January/February - "Dolly Dingle's Little Friends, Gwennie and Denny Sweetie"
March - "Dolly Dingle's Little Playmate, Dotty Heard"
April - "Two More Of the Sweetie Children - Jennie and Benny"
May - "Dolly Dingle's Little Friend Peggy"
June - "Sammy Gets Ready For the Baseball Season"
July/August - "Dolly Dingle's Little Friend Maxine and Her New Dresses"
September - "Dolly Dingle's Little Cousin Peter"
October - "Dolly Dingle's Little Playmate Marietta"
November - "Dolly Dingle's Little Cousin Leonard"

1921

January - "Dolly Dingle Has A Party For Poor Little Polly" (two pages)
February - "Dolly Dingle Takes Up Grand Opera - *Carmen*"
March - "Dolly Dingle Takes Up Grand Opera -

Pagliacci"

April - "Dolly Dingle Takes Up Grand Opera - *La Boheme*"

May - "Dolly Dingle Takes Up Light Opera - *The Mikado*"

June - "Dolly Dingle Takes Up Light Opera - *H.M.S. Pinafore*"

July - "Dolly Dingle Takes Up Light Opera - *Erminie*"

August - "Dolly Dingle Takes Up Grand Opera - *Don Giovanni*"

September - "Dolly Dingle's Fairy Tales - *Little Red Riding Hood*"

October - "Dolly Dingle's Fairy Tales - *Hansel and Gretel*"

November - "Dolly Dingle Plays 'The Courtship of Miles Standish' "

December - "Dollie Dingle and Tommy and Bessie and Sammy Send Christmas Greetings To All Their Little Friends" (two pages)

1922

January - "Dolly Dingle and Sammy Go Skating"

February - "Dolly Dingle, Bobby Blake, and the Story of Little Mary"

March - "Dolly Dingle and Neddy and the Story of Artie and Baldie"

April - "Dolly Dingle and the Stories of Mrs. Mousie and Bumpty"

May - "Dolly Dingle, Tommy, and the Story of Kittie Cutie"

June - "Dolly Dingle, Johnny, and the Story of Fido"

July - "Dolly Dingle's Little Friends Peggy-Anne and Joel"

August - "Dolly Dingle's Little Friends Janet and Jackie"

September - "Dolly Dingle Dingle Makes A Cake and Pudding"

October - "Dolly Dingle's Little Friend Barbara"

November - "Dolly Dingle Makes A Dress and Darns Socks"

December - "Dolly Dingle's Busy Christmas" (two pages)

1923

January - "Dolly Dingle Goes Snow-Shoeing"

February - "Dolly Dingle's Baby Brother Dickie"

March - "Dolly Dingle's Fido Dresses Up"

April - "Dolly Dingle's Kitty Dresses Up"

May - "Dolly Dingle's Brother Plays Farmer"

June - "Dolly Dingle's Gowns and Faces"

July - "Dollie Dingle Shows How To Keep Well"

August - "Dollie Dingle Learns Some Nice Rules"

September - "Dottie Dumpling Helps Mother Prepare Luncheon"

October - "Dolly Dingle and Sammy Smart Help Teacher"

November - "Dolly Dingle's Big Sister Maxine"

December - "Dolly Dingle's Cousin Peggy Anne" (This paper doll also appeared in January 1932)

December - "Dolly Dingle's Christmas Cards"

1924

January - "Dolly Dingle's Little Friend Joey Goes To A Carnival"

February - "Dolly Dingle's Pretty Little Friend Teedie"

March - "Dolly Dingle's Little Cousin Robin" (This paper doll also appeared March 1932)

April - "Dolly Dingle's Little Friend Mary Lamb With Fancy Dress Costumes"

May - "Dolly Dingle's Little Friend Junior Allen and Tinker"

June - "Dolly Dingle's Little Friend Gracie Harriman and Fluffles"

July - "Dolly Dingle's Paper Dolls and Her Little Friend Julie"

August - "Dolly Dingle's Paper Dolls and Her Little Friend Roddy"

September - "Dolly Dingle's Little Friends Elsie and Max Have A Happy Vacation"

October - "Dolly Dingle's Little Friends Joan and Jock With Their Pets"

November - "Dolly Dingle and Mama Dingle As She Was Twenty-Five Years Ago"

December - "Just A Few Of Dolly Dingle's Christmas Presents"

December - "Dolly Dingle's Christmas Cards"

1925

January - "The Betty Bobbs Family - Introducing Betty Bobbs Herself"

February - "The Betty Bobbs Family - Betty's Baby Brother Buddy Bobbs"

March - "The Pin-A-Peep Show - Cinderella" (stand-up figures)

May - "The Betty Bobbs Family - Betty's Older Sister Bonnie Bobbs"

June - "The Pin-A-Peep Show - Hansel and Gretel" (stand-up figures)

July - "The Betty Bobbs Family - Betty's Older Brother Bobby Bobbs"

August - "The Pin-A-Peep Show - Snow White" (stand-up figures)

September - "The Pin-A-Peep Show - Little Red Riding Hood" (stand-up figures)

October - "The Pin-a-Peep Show - The Six Swans" (stand-up figures)

November - "Animated Toy Cut-Outs - Fun At The Amusement Park" (paper toy)

December - "Animated Toy Cut-Outs - The Christmas Tree" (paper toy)

1926

January - "Peggy Pryde and Her Playmates"

February - "Peggy Pryde's Little Brother Peter"

March - "Peggy Pryde's Cousin Carrie"
April - "Peggy Pryde's Sister Patty"
May - "Peggy Pryde's Athletic Brother Phil"
June - "Dolly Dingle's Friends Return (Marie Louise)"
July - "Dolly Dingle and Her Dollies"
August - "Dolly Dingle's Friend Sunny"
September - "Dolly Dingle's Little Friend Tottie"
October - "Dolly Dingle's Cousin Carol"
November - "Dolly Dingle's WeekEnd Guest Virginia"
December - "Dolly Dingle's Greetings" (Christmas cards)

1927
January - "Dolly Dingle"
February - "Dolly Dingle's Valentine"
March - "Dolly Dingle As Cinderella"
April - "Dolly Dingle's Cousin"
May - "Dolly Dingle's Boy Friend (Johnny Jones)"
June - "Dolly Dingle's Nephew"
July - "Dolly Dingle's Playmate (Evangeline Mary)"
August - "Dolly Dingle's Sweetheart (Lucian)"
September - "Dolly Dingle's Vacation (Sibyl)"
October - "Dolly Dingle's Hallowe'en"
November - "Dolly Dingle's Young Visitor (Leonora)"

1928
January - "Dolly Dingle's Hawaiian Flight"
February - "Dolly Dingle Visits Japan"
March - "Dolly Dingle Flies To Russia"
April - "Dolly Dingle's Cousin Lindy"
May - "Dolly Dingle's Friend Douglas"
June - "Dolly Dingle's Trip To Persia"
July - "Dolly Dingle Flies To China"
August - "Dolly Dingle Takes A Vacation"

1929
February - "The Adventures of Dolly Dingle"
March - "Dolly Dingle's Cousin Bill"
April - "Dolly Dingle's Adventures"
May - "Dolly Dingle's Playmates (Billie)"
June - "Dolly Dingle's Cousin Marion" (same paper doll as March 1930)
July - "Dolly Dingle's Sweetheart (Billie)"
August - "Dolly Dingle's WeekEnd"
September - "Dolly Dingle's Travels"
October - "Dolly Dingle As Bridesmaid (Nanny)"
November - "Dolly Dingle At The Party"
December - "Dolly Dingle's Christmas (Jane)"

1930
January - "Dolly Dingle's Little Guest (Betty)"
February - "Dolly Dingle's Twin Cousins (Jock and Joan)"
March - "Dolly Dingle's Party" (same paper doll as June 1929)
April - "Dolly Dingle's Boy Friend (Tommy)"

May - "Dolly Dingle (Daisy and Baby Doll)"
June - "Dolly Dingle (Brother and Sister)"
July - "Dolly Dingle (Bud)"
August - "Dolly Dingle"
September - "Dolly Dingle"
October - "Dolly Dingle (Joe)"
November - "Dolly Dingle"
December - "Dolly Dingle"

1931
January - "Dolly Dingle"
February - "Dolly Dingle"
April - "Dolly Dingle"
May - "Dolly Dingle"
June - "Dolly Dingle"
July - "Dolly Dingle"
August - "Dolly Dingle"
September - "Dolly Dingle"

1932
January - "Dolly Dingle's Cousin" (This paper doll also appeared in December 1923)
February - "A Washington Birthday Party" (No outfits for the dolls. These paper dolls also appeared in February 1919.)
March - "Dolly Dingle" (This paper doll also appeared in March 1924)
April - "Dolly Dingle's World Flight - The Start"
May - "Dolly Dingle's World Flight - In England"
June - "Dolly Dingle's World Flight - In France"
August - "Dolly Dingle's World Flight - In Germany"
September - "Dolly Dingle's World Flight - In Switzerland"
October - "Dolly Dingle's World Flight - In Holland"
November - "Dolly Dingle's World Flight - In Denmark"
December - "Dolly Dingle's World Flight - In Italy"

1933
January - "Dolly Dingle's World Flight - In Burgundy"
February - "Dolly Dingle's World flight - In Sweden"
March - "Dolly Dingle's World Flight - In Russia"
April - "Dolly Dingle"

This ends the "Dolly Dingle" series of paper dolls.

May - "Introducing Polly and Peter Perkins"
June - "Adventures of Polly and Peter Perkins"
July - "Adventures of Polly and Peter Perkins"
August - "Adventures of Polly and Peter Perkins"
September - "Adventures of Polly and Peter Perkins"
October - "Dottie Darling Goes To A Halloween Party"
November - "Dottie Darling's Country Cousin,

Tommy Tucker"

December - "Adventures of Polly and Peter Perkins"

1934

January - "Dottie Darling's Friend Flora McFlimsy"

February - "Adventures of Polly and Peter Perkins"

March - "Dottie Darling's Little Friend Sunny Sammy"

April - "Adventures of Polly and Peter Perkins"

May - "Dottie Darling's Friend Merry Mary - And

Her Gamboling Lamb"

June - "Adventures of Polly and Peter Perkins"

July - "Dottie Darling's Boy Friend - Huskie Horace"

August - "Adventures of Polly and Peter Perkins"

September - "Dottie Darling's Sister Susie Goes Back To School"

October - "Adventures of Polly and Peter Perkins"

November - "Adventures of Polly and Peter Perkins"

December - "Dottie Darling's Brother Bobbie Dresses As Santa Claus"

April 1909

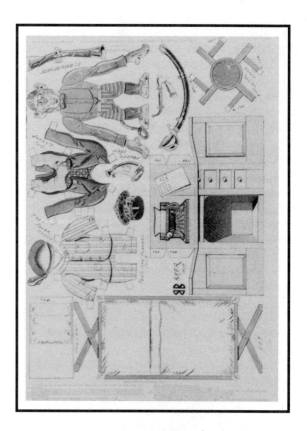

May 1909

Both courtesy of Virginia Crossley

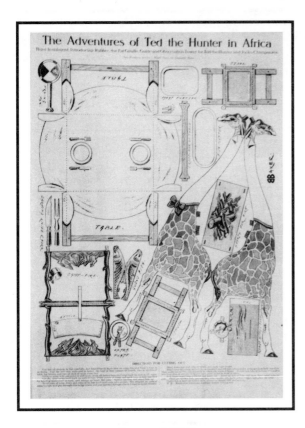

June 1909
Courtesy of Virginia Crossley

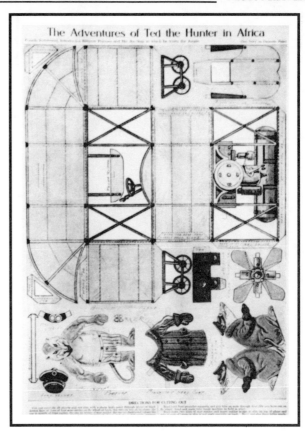

September 1909
Courtesy of Virginia Crossley

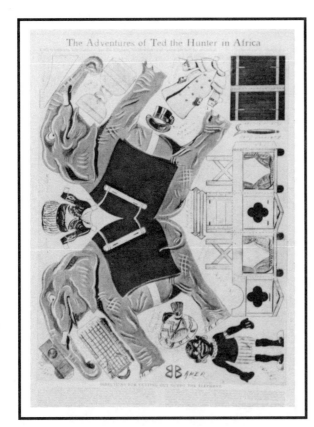

October 1909
Courtesy of Virginia Crossley

December 1909
Courtesy of Janie Varsolona

The other three pages in this "Alice In Wonderland" series (November 1909, January and February 1910) were not available for photographing.

March 1913
Courtesy of Rosalie Eppert

April 1913
Courtesy of Emy Varsolona

May 1913
Courtesy of Rosalie Eppert

June 1913
Courtesy of Rosalie Eppert

Even though the following nine pictures are not paper dolls, they are by the same artist (Grace G. Drayton) that drew the "Dolly Dingle" paper dolls and are just as collectible as the paper dolls.

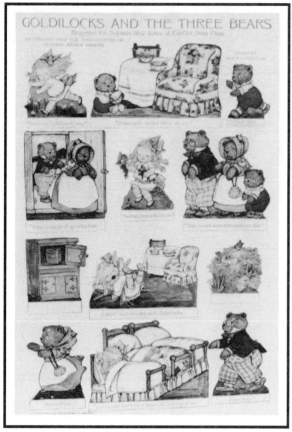

October 1913

December 1913

January 1914

February 1914

March 1914
Courtesy of Virginia Crossley

April 1914
Courtesy of Virginia Crossley

May 1914
Courtesy of Virginia Crossley

December 1914
From the Jane Sugg Collection

January 1916
From the Jane Sugg Collection

March 1916

April 1916
Courtesy of Virginia Crossley

May 1916

June 1916

July 1916

August 1916

September 1916
Courtesy of Virginia Crossley

October 1916

November 1916

December 1916

January 1917

February 1917

March 1917

April 1917

May 1917

June 1917

July 1917

August 1917

September 1917

October 1917

November 1917

December 1917
(The first page of two)

December 1917
(The second page of two)

January 1918

February 1918

March 1918
Courtesy of Virginia Crossley

April 1918

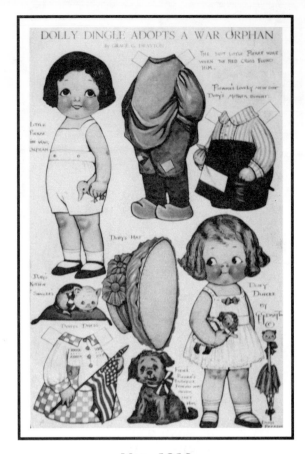

May 1918

June 1918
Courtesy of Virginia Crossley

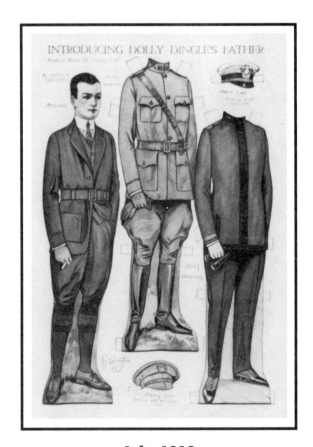

July 1918

August 1918

September 1918
Courtesy of Virginia Crossley

October 1918
Courtesy of Virginia Crossley

November 1918

December 1918
Courtesy of Virginia Crossley

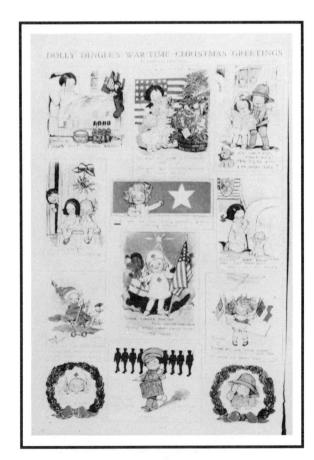

December 1918
Courtesy of Virginia Crossley

January 1919
Courtesy of Virginia Crossley

January 1919
Courtesy of Virginia Crossley

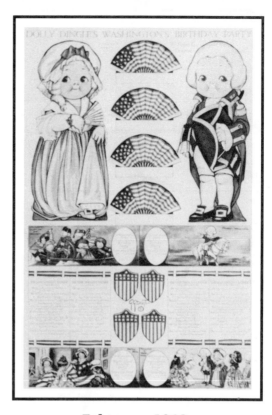

February 1919
These paper dolls were also in February 1932. To help identify cut sets, the boy is almost 7½" tall on this page and only 6½" tall on the February 1932 page.

March 1919

April 1919
Courtesy of Virginia Crossley

May 1919

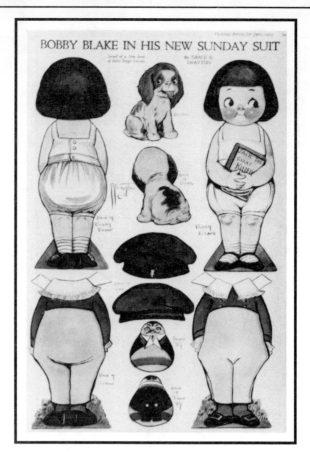

June 1919

July 1919

August 1919
Courtesy of Virginia Crossley

September 1919
Courtesy of Virginia Crossley

October 1919
Courtesy of Virginia Crossley

October 1919
Courtesy of Virginia Crossley

November 1919
Courtesy of Virginia Crossley

January/February 1920

March 1920

April 1920

May 1920

June 1920
Courtesy of Virginia Crossley

July/August 1920

September 1920

October 1920
Courtesy of Virginia Crossley

November 1920

January 1921
(The first page of two)
Courtesy of Virginia Crossley

January 1921
(The second page of two)
Courtesy of Virginia Crossley

February 1921
Courtesy of Virginia Crossley

March 1921
Courtesy of Virginia Crossley

April 1921
Courtesy of Virginia Crossley

May 1921
Courtesy of Virginia Crossley

June 1921

July 1921
Courtesy of Virginia Crossley

August 1921
Courtesy of Virginia Crossley

September 1921

October 1921

November 1921

December 1921
(The first page of two)
Courtesy of Virginia Crossley

December 1921
(The second page of two)
Courtesy of Virginia Crossley

January 1922

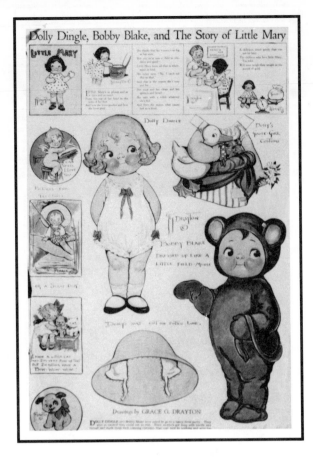

February 1922

March 1922
Courtesy of Virginia Crossley

April 1922

May 1922

June 1922
Courtesy of Virginia Crossley

July 1922
Courtesy of Virginia Crossley

August 1922

September 1922

October 1922

November 1922

December 1922
Courtesy of Emy Varsolona

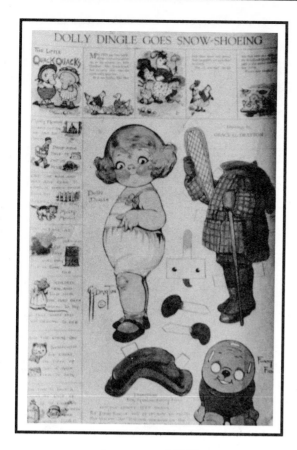

January 1923
Courtesy of Virginia Crossley

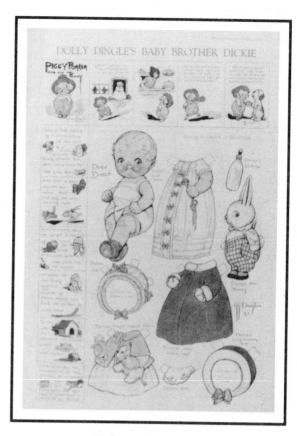

February 1923
Courtesy of Virginia Crossley

March 1923

April 1923

May 1923

June 1923

July 1923

August 1923

September 1923

October 1923

November 1923

December 1923
This paper doll was also in January 1932. To help identify cut sets, the doll on this page is 7¼" tall and only 7" tall on the January 1932 page.

December 1923
From the Louise Kaufman Collection

January 1924

February 1924

March 1924
This paper doll was also in March 1932. To help identify cut sets, the sailor suit is blue on this page and red on the March 1932 page.

April 1924

May 1924

June 1924

July 1924

August 1924

September 1924

October 1924

November 1924

December 1924

December 1924
Courtesy of Jenny Elmore

January 1925

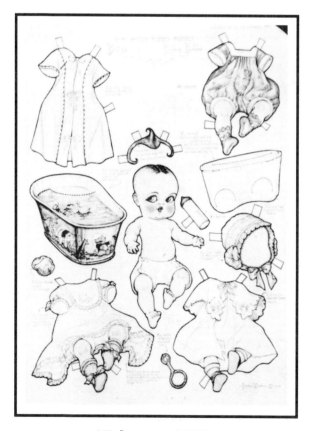

February 1925

March 1925
This is one example of "The Pin-a-Peep Show" series. Stand-up figures are included but not paper dolls.

May 1925

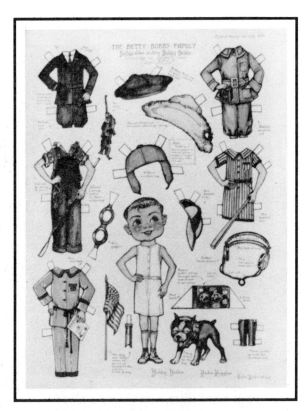

July 1925
Courtesy of Virginia Crossley

January 1926

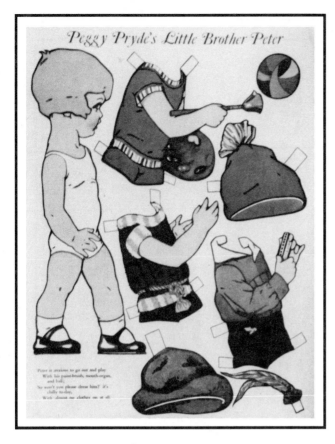

February 1926

March 1926

April 1926

May 1926

June 1926

July 1926

August 1926

September 1926
Courtesy of Virginia Crossley

October 1926

November 1926

December 1926
Courtesy of Virginia Crossley

January 1927

February 1927
Courtesy of Virginia Crossley

March 1927

April 1927

May 1927

June 1927
Courtesy of Virginia Crossley

July 1927

August 1927

September 1927

October 1927

November 1927

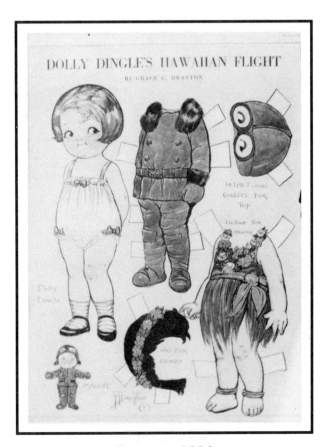

January 1928

February 1928

March 1928

April 1928
Courtesy of Virginia Crossley

May 1928
Courtesy of Virginia Crossley

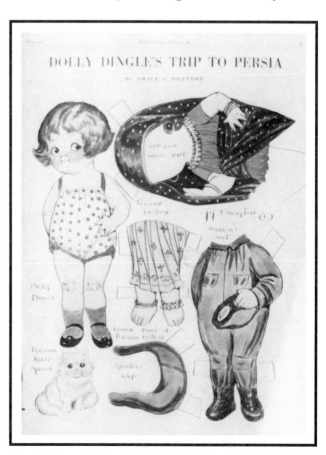

June 1928

July 1928

August 1928

February 1929

March 1929

April 1929

May 1929

June 1929
This paper doll was also in March 1930. To help identify cut sets, dark colors are black/grey on this page and blue/black on the March 1930 page.

July 1929

August 1929

September 1929

October 1929

November 1929

December 1929

January 1930

February 1930

March 1930
This paper doll was also in June 1929. To help identify cut sets, dark colors are blue/black on this page and are grey/black on the June 1929 page.

April 1930

May 1930

June 1930

July 1930
Courtesy of Virginia Crossley

August 1930

September 1930

October 1930
Courtesy of Virginia Crossley

November 1930
Courtesy of Virginia Crossley

December 1930
Courtesy of Virginia Crossley

January 1931
Courtesy of Virginia Crossley

February 1931

April 1931
Courtesy of Virginia Crossley

May 1931
Courtesy of Virginia Crossley

June 1931
Courtesy of Virginia Crossley

July 1931

August 1931
Courtesy of Virginia Crossley

September 1931
Courtesy of Virginia Crossley

January 1932
Courtesy of Virginia Crossley
This paper doll was also in December 1923. The doll on this page is 7" tall and 7¼" tall on the December 1923 page.

February 1932
These paper dolls were also in February 1919. To help identify cut sets, the boy is 6½" tall on this page and almost 7½" tall on the February 1919 page.

March 1932
This paper doll was also in March 1924. To help identify cut sets, the sailor suit is red on this page and blue on the March 1924 page.

April 1932
Courtesy of Virginia Crossley

May 1932
Courtesy of Virginia Crossley

June 1932
Courtesy of Virginia Crossley

August 1932

September 1932

October 1932

November 1932

December 1932
Courtesy of Virginia Crossley

January 1933

February 1933

March 1933

April 1933

May 1933

June 1933

July 1933

August 1933

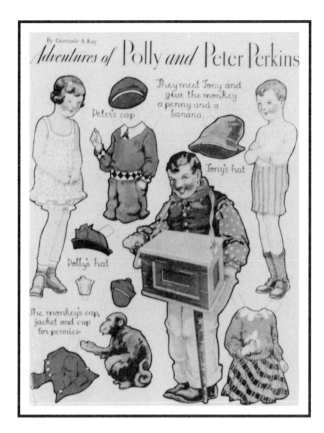

September 1933

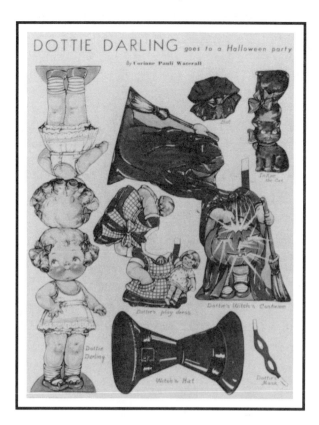

October 1933
Courtesy of Virginia Crossley

November 1933

December 1933

January 1934

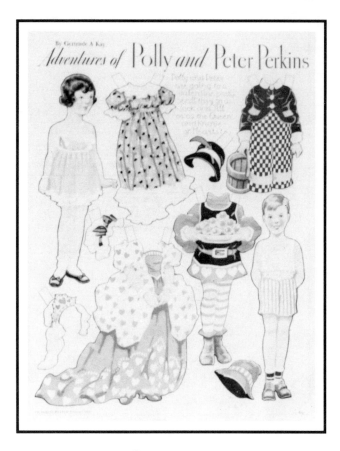

February 1934

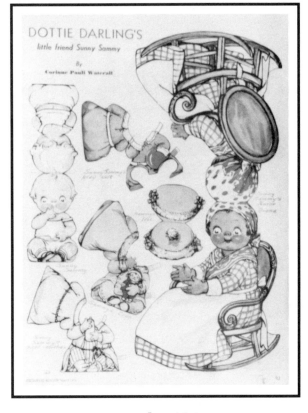

March 1934
Courtesy of Virginia Crossley

April 1934

May 1934

June 1934

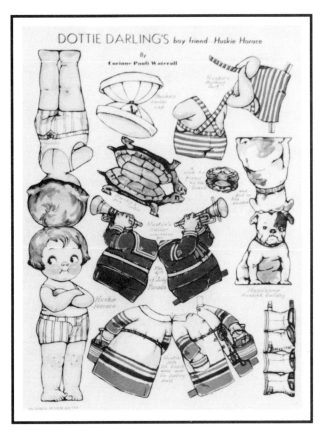

July 1934

August 1934

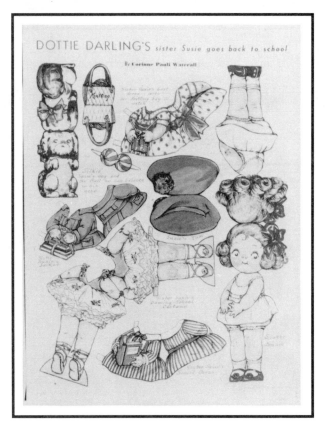

September 1934
Courtesy of Virginia Crossley

October 1934

November 1934

December 1934

The Prairie Farmer

February 9, 1924
"Our Junior Page - Polly Peters"
Courtesy of Helen Johnson

Primary Education - Popular Educator

The teacher's magazine of *Primary Education* had its start in 1893 and united with *Popular Educator* in 1926. *Popular Educator* had an earlier beginning in 1885 in Boston. When the two magazines merged, they were known as *Primary Education - Popular Educator* until March 1929 when the name was changed to *The Grade Teacher* (covered elsewhere in this book).

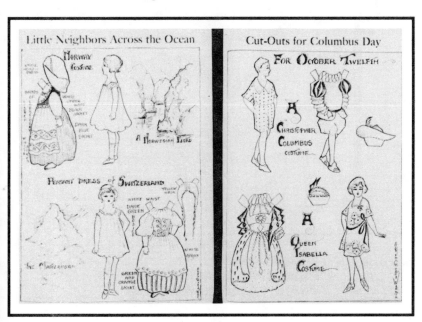

September 1928
"Little Neighbors Across The Ocean"

October 1928
"Cut-Outs For Columbus Day"

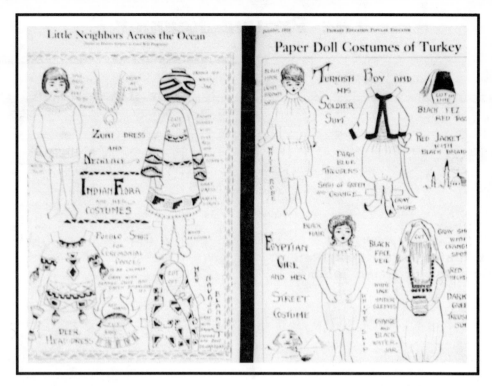

**November 1928
"Little Neighbors
Across The Ocean"**

**December 1928
"Paper Doll Costumes
Of Turkey"**

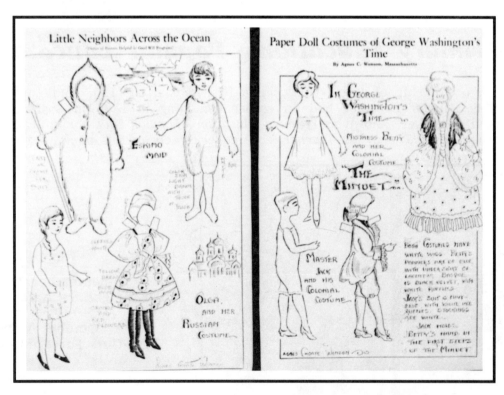

**January 1929
"Little Neighbors
Across The Ocean"**

**February 1929
"Paper Doll Costumes Of
George Washington's Time"**

(This series of paper dolls was continued in *The Grade Teacher*.)

Screen Life

A paper doll series of "Star Dolls" began with "Judy Garland" in February 1941. (Not available for picture.)

**March 1941
"Screen Life's Star Dolls
(No. 2) Clark Gable"
Courtesy of Emma Terry**

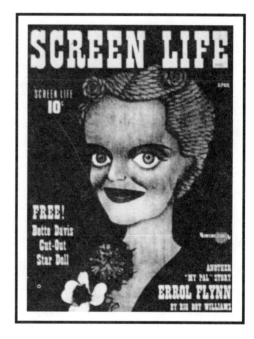

Screen Life **Cover
April 1941
Courtesy of Pat Dahlberg**

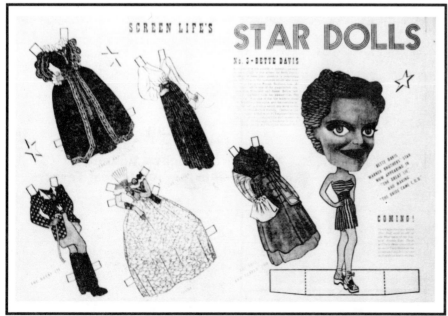

**April 1941
"Screen Life's Star Dolls
(No. 3) Bette Davis"
Courtesy of Pat Dahlberg**

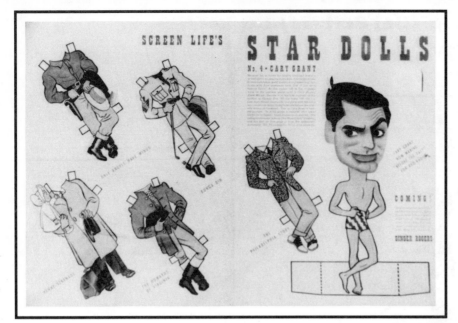

**May 1941
"Screen Life's Star Dolls
(No. 4) Cary Grant"
Courtesy of Rosalie Eppert**

**June 1941
"Screen Life's Star Dolls
Ginger Rogers"
Courtesy of Emma Terry**

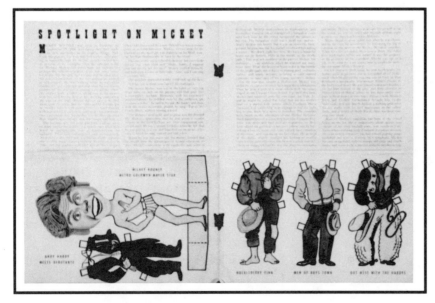

**July 1941
"Spotlight On Mickey -
Mickey Rooney"
Courtesy of Emma Terry**

Simplicity Pattern Magazine

November/December 1934
"Winnie"
(The paper doll appeared on the back cover of the magazine.)

Fall/Winter 1949
"Simplicity Jane"
(date not verified)

1950
"Simplicity Joan"
(date not verified)

1950
"Simplicty Jack"
(date not verified)

1950
"Simplicity Kate"
(date not verified)

1951
"Simplicity Tom"
(date not verified)

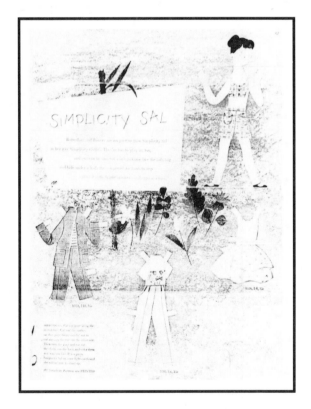

1951
"Simplicity Sal"
(date not verified)
Courtesy of Jean Sullivan

Today's Magazine

Today's Magazine was published in New York from 1905 until 1928. After 1917, it was known as Today's Housewife. The three paper doll pages shown are all that could be found from this magazine. The paper dolls are known as the "Polka Dots" (the clown is Polka and the little girl is Dot). Also on each page is "Mother Hubbard's Cupboard" which is a letter to the children.

August 1914
"Mother Hubbard's Cupboard
The Polka Dot Cut-Outs"
Courtesy of Rosalie Eppert

October 1914
"The Polka Dots And
The Rocking Leopard"
Courtesy of Shirley Hedge

January 1915
"The Polka Dots Learn To Fence"
Courtesy of Helen Johnson

Vanity Fair

Vanity Fair was published from 1913 to 1936.

September 1933
"Vanity Fair's Own Paper Dolls
(No. 1) (J.P. Morgan)
Courtesy of Carol Carey

November 1933
"Vanity Fair's Own Paper Dolls
(No. 2) (Aimee MacPherson Hutton)
Courtesy of Carol Carey

January 1934
"Vanity Fair's Own Paper Dolls
(No. 3) (Prince of Wales)

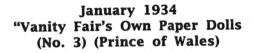

**February 1934
"The Grand Duchess
Marie Paper Doll"**

**March 1934
"Vanity Fair's Own Paper Dolls
(No. 5) (Earnest Hemingway)"
Courtesy of Donna Heiser**

**April 1934
"Vanity Fair's Own Paper Dolls
(No. 6) (Albert Einstein)"
Courtesy of Janie Varsolona**

**May 1934
"Vanity Fair's Own Paper Dolls
(No. 7) (Heywood Campbell Broun)"
Courtesy of Donna Heiser**

Woman's Day

Woman's Day began publishing in 1937.

August 1954
"Real Fabric Clothes For A Paper Doll"
Courtesy of Rosalie Eppert

Woman's Home Companion

The *Woman's Home Companion* was published in Springfield, Ohio. The magazine began in 1873 and ended with the January 1957 issue. From 1873 to 1895 the magazine was known as *Ladies' Home Companion*.

The following is a list of the known cut-out children's pages which appeared in *Woman's Home Companion*. The paper doll pages are pictured following the list.

1912
October - "The First of the Kewpie Kutouts - Presenting Wag, the Kewpie Chief; Dotty Darling and Dotty Darling's Baby Brother."
November - "The Kewpie Kutouts - Presenting the Kewpie Cook and Dotty Darling's Mother."
December - "Stern Irene and the Kewpie Gardener - Third in the Series of Kewpie Kutouts."

1913
January - "The Kewpie Kutouts - Presenting the One That's Careful of His Voice and Dotty Darling's Sister Nan."

February - "The Kewpie Kutouts - Presenting the One Who Always Wears His Overshoes and Dotty Darling's Brother Dan."
March - "The Kewpie Kutouts - The Kewpie Army and the Orphan Boy."
April - "The Kewpies and Father Darling" (This is not a paper doll or cut-out page)
May - "The Flying Kewpies - A New and Fascinating Kewpish Family."
June - "The Kewpie Kutouts - Little Assunta and Her Kewpie Doll."
July - "Dotty and Four Of Her Kewpie Friends"
August - "The Musical Kewpies - and the Little

German Girl."

September - "The Wealthy Kewpie and the Wealthy Child"

October - "The Kewpie Nurse and the Better Baby"

December - "The Kewpie Dog and the Bad Little Boy"

1914

January - "Flying Kewpies - Who Want To Fly About Your Christmas Tree" (This issue also contains an article written and illustrated by Rose O'Neill titled "The Coming of the Kewpies - For Children and Grown-Ups Kewpishly Inclined.")

February - "A Kewpie Valentine"

Each issue that contained a Kewpie paper doll page had a companion page of verses and illustrations by Rose O'Neill.

A children's page that could be cut and folded into a small book titled "The Adventures of Jack and Betty," began in 1913, and appeared intermittently in 1914 and the early months of 1915.

1915

In September 1915 the "Jack and Betty Magazine" page began. Like the preceding "Jack and Betty" series, this page could also be cut and folded to form a magazine.

1916

March - "A Paper Doll That Betty and Jeannette Made" (on the "Jack and Betty" magazine page)

1917

November - "Little Folks Own Circus" (stand-up figures)

December - "Little Folks Own Circus" (stand-up figures)

1918

February - "Little Folks Own Circus" (stand-up figures)

March - "Little Folks Own Circus" (stand-up figures)

June - "Little Folks Own Circus" (stand-up figures)

August - "Little Folks Own Circus" (stand-up figures)

November - "Little Folks Own Circus" (stand-up figures)

December - "Little Folks Own Circus" (stand-up figures)

1919

January - "Little Folks Play Friends" (stand-up figures)

February - "Little Folks Play Friends" (stand-up figures)

figures)

May - "Little Folks Play Friends" (stand-up figures)

June - "Little Folks Play Friends" (stand-up figures)

July - "Little Folks Play Friends" (stand-up figures)

August - "Little Folks Play Friends" (stand-up figures)

October - "Little Folks Play Friends" (stand-up figures)

November - "Trips To Mother Goose Land" (stand-up figures)

Cover of *Woman's Home Companion*, November 1916

1920

January - "Trips To Mother Goose Land" (stand-up figures)

February - "The Companion Paper Doll - Introducing Margery May"

April - "The Companion Paper Doll - Here Is Margery May's Little Cousin, Suzette"

May - "Trips To Mother Goose Land" (stand-up figures)

June - "The Companion Paper Doll - This month we see Margery May's Brother, Tom"

July - "Trips To Mother Goose Land" (stand-up figures)

August - "The Companion Paper Doll - Margery May's French Chum, Marie Louise"

September - "Trips To Mother Goose Land" (stand-up figures)
October - "Trips To Mother Goose Land" (stand-up figures)
November - "The Companion Paper Doll - Here Are The Twins, Margery May's Little Sisters."

1921
January - "Trips To Mother Goose Land" (stand-up figures)
February - "Trips To Mother Goose Land" (stand-up figures)
March - "The Companion Paper Doll - Margery May's Japanese Friend, Tamaki"
April - "Trips To Mother Goose Land" (stand-up figures)
June - "Margery May's Big Sister"

1922
July - "The Make-Your-Own Model Airplane" (paper toy)
November - "The Little Busybodies - Katy Curls"

1923
January - "The Second Of The Little Busybodies - Reddy Teddy"
February - "The Little Busybodies - Jolly Jane"
March - "The Little Busybodies - Bunny Boy"
June - "The Fifth of the Little Busybodies - Puggy Pam"
August - "The Sixth Little Busybody - Rob the Rogue"

November - "The Twins - The New Paper Dolls For Children"

1924
January - "Punch and Judy, The Twins - The New Paper Dolls That Grow Older. Here They Are At Two Years."
April - "The Twins - The Paper Dolls That Grow Older - Now They Are Four."
July - "The Twins - Paper Dolls That Grow Older"
December - "Cut-Outs For the Tree" (paper baskets to be filled with candy and popcorn)

1925
May - "Jackie Coogan"
June - "The Baby Peggy Paper Doll"
August - "Peter Pan"
October - "Our Gang As Paper Dolls"

1926
September - "Madeline of Maine"
November - "Texas Tom"

1927
February - "Winifred of Wisconsin"
April - "Carl of California"
June - "Katy Of Kentucky"

1937
March - An advertising paper doll appeared this month and is pictured at the back of the book with other advertising paper dolls.

1942
January - "Rosita" (two pages)

1943
January - "We Decorate Mrs. Paper Doll's Living Room" (paper furniture, two pages)

1956
October - "Must Your Husband Look That Way?"

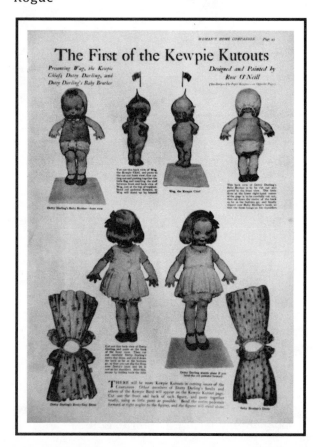

October 1912
Courtesy of Virginia Crossley

November 1912

December 1912

January 1913

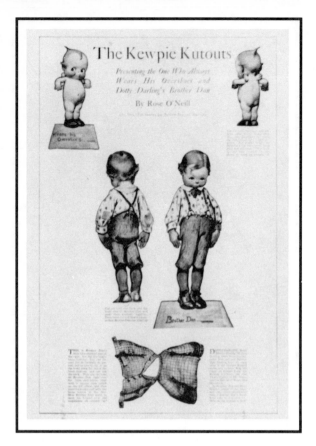

February 1913

March 1913

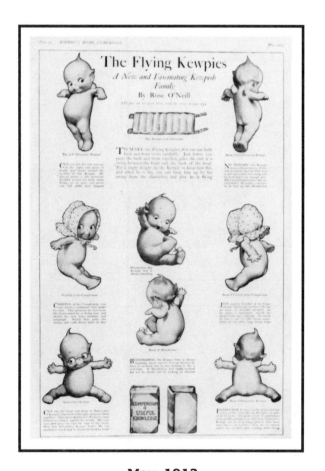

May 1913

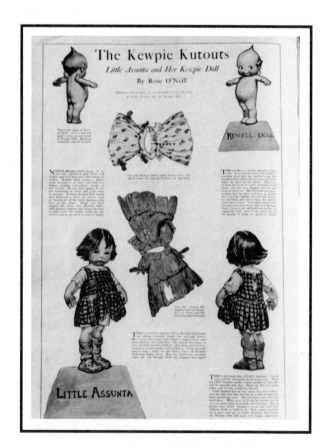

June 1913

July 1913

August 1913

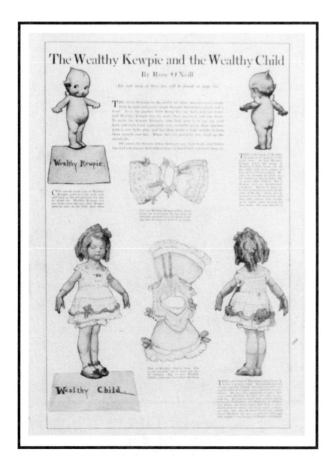

September 1913

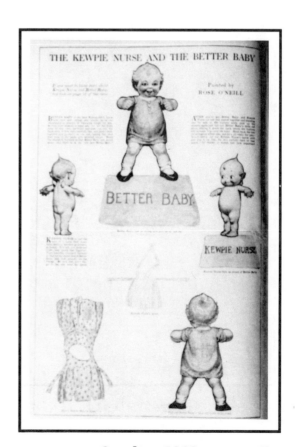

October 1913

December 1913

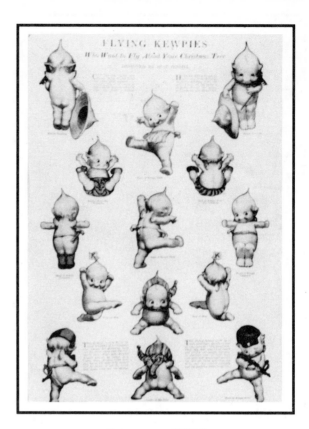

January 1914

February 1914

March 1916
(This paper doll is
in black and white.)

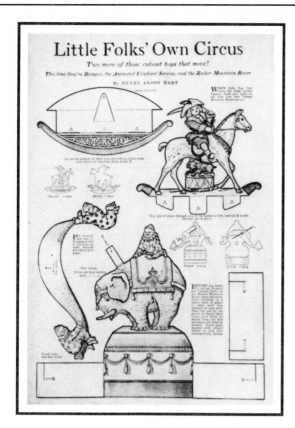

March 1918
This is one example of the
"Little Folks Own Circus."

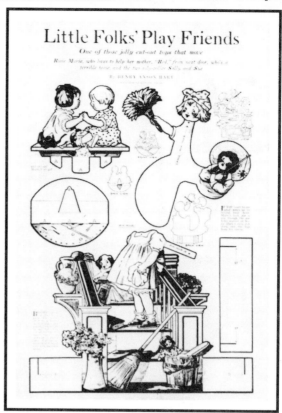

October 1919
This is one example of the
"Little Folks Play Friends."
Courtesy of Wynn Yusas

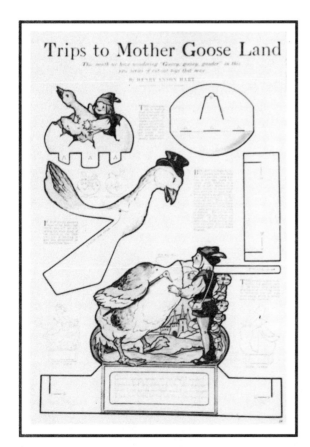

April 1921
This is one example of the
"Trips To Mother Goose Land."

February 1920

April 1920
Courtesy of Virginia Crossley

June 1920
Courtesy of Virginia Crossley

August 1920
Courtesy of Virginia Crossley

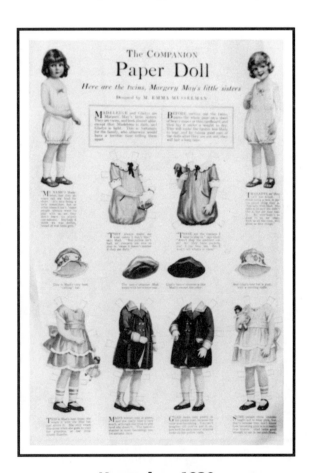

November 1920

March 1921

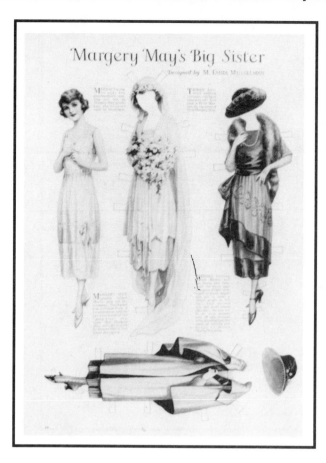

June 1921
Courtesy of Virginia Crossley

November 1922

January 1923

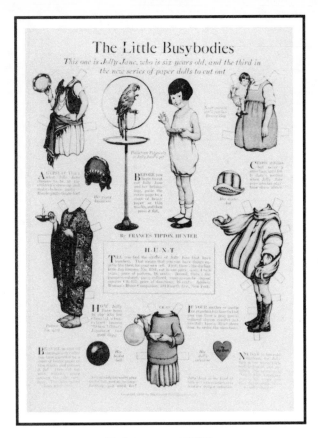

February 1923
Courtesy of Virginia Crossley

March 1923

June 1923
Courtesy of Virginia Crossley

August 1923
Courtesy of Virginia Crossley

November 1923

January 1924

April 1924

July 1924

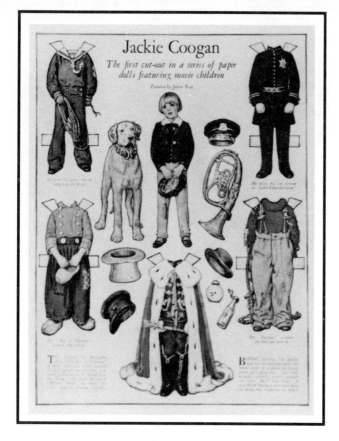

May 1925

June 1925

August 1925
Courtesy of Virginia Crossley

October 1925
Courtesy of Virginia Crossley

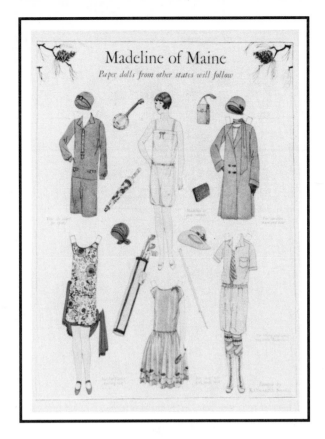

September 1926

November 1926

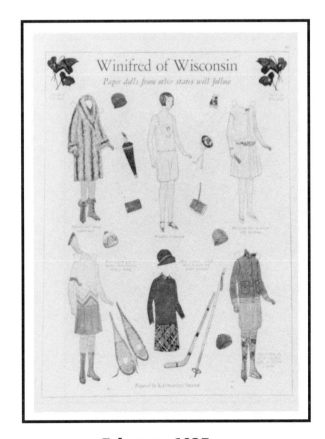

February 1927

April 1927

All paper dolls on this page courtesy of Virginia Crossley.

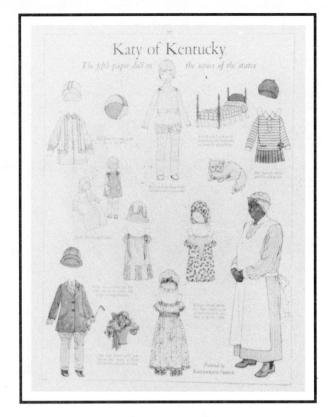

June 1927
Courtesy of Virginia Crossley

October 1956
Courtesy of Shirley Hedge

January 1942

The Woman's Magazine

The Woman's Magazine was published from 1896 to 1920, and then it united with *Designer* to form *Designer and The Woman's Magazine*. From 1896 to March 1912, the magazine was known as *New Idea Woman's Magazine.*

A cut-and-paste picture page, "Cecil and Cissy In Circleland," appeared in a few issues of 1912 and 1913 and possibly in the preceding years also.

In March 1913, a series of jointed paper dolls began. Other known paper dolls from *The Woman's Magazine* are also pictured.

March 1913
"Jean - Our Jointed Paper Doll"
Courtesy of Helen Johnson

April 1913
"The Jointed Paper Doll Family"
(Jean's Young Lady Sister)
Courtesy of Virginia Crossley

**June 1913
"3. Katie of the Jointed
Paper Doll Family"
Courtesy of Rosalie Eppert**

**July 1913
"Two More Members of
Our Jointed Paper Doll Family IV -
Baby Polly and Her
Irish Nurse, Norah"
Courtesy of Rosalie Eppert**

**September 1913
"The Jointed Paper Doll Family V
At The Seashore With
Katie's Big Sister, Mary Louise!"
From the Jane Sugg Collection**

**May 1914
"Dick - Our Jointed
Paper Doll Boy Scout"
Courtesy of Marianne Anderson**

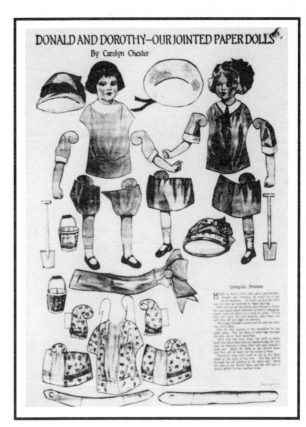

**August 1914
"Donald and Dorothy -
Our Jointed Paper Dolls"
Courtesy of Helen Johnson**

**January 1915
"Little Sister - Our New
Back-And-Front Doll"
Courtesy of Rosalie Eppert**

February 1915
"Little Brother - With Back and Front"
Courtesy of Rosalie Eppert

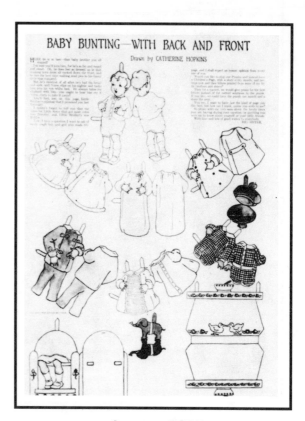

August 1915
"Baby Bunting - With Back and Front"
Courtesy of Helen Johnson

March 1916
"Susette Our Jointed Paper Doll"
(black and white page)
Courtesy of Helen Johnson

May 1917
"Mistress Mary"
Courtesy of Helen Johnson

June 1917
"Chin-Chin From China"
Courtesy of Helen Johnson

January 1918
"Toinette La Petite"

March 1918
"Natascha Of Russia"
Courtesy of Rosalie Eppert

June 1918
"Strong-Arm" and "Nimble-Fingers"
Courtesy of Virginia Crossley

July 1918
"Little Miss Columbia"
Courtesy of Rosalie Eppert

August 1919
"Rosalind From London Town"
Courtesy of Rosalie Eppert

November 1919
"Launcelot Marmaduke Fauntleroy ... "
Courtesy of Virginia Crossley

December 1919
"It's Never Winter Where We Stay;
Our Carrots Grow In A Magic Way ..."
Courtesy of Virginia Crossley

March 1920
"Oh, We're Three Famous Kittens ..."
Courtesy of Ilene Duluk

Advertising Pages With Paper Dolls

The advertising paper doll pages may have appeared in more than one magazine.

"Fashion Parade Of The Month ... May" This page appeared in *Canadian Home Journal* in May 1937. The same page appeared in *Woman's Home Companion* in March 1937. The only difference is the name of the month at the top of the page.

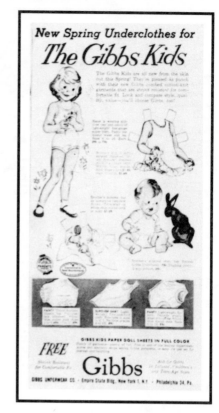

**"Fashion Parade
Of The Month ... June"**
This page appeared in *Pictorial
Review* in June 1937. Both this
page and the ad on the previous
page advertise Cutex nail polish.

**"New Spring
Underclothes For the
Gibbs Kids"**
This advertisement appeared in *Good House-
keeping* in April 1952.

**"Springmaid Cotton Broadcloth
Is Cut Out For You!"**
This page appeared in April 1951 in *Good
Housekeeping.*

**"A Quadriga Cut-Out Stanley Musial
(and his son, Dickie)"**
This page appeared in *Life,*
April 26, 1948

"A Quadriga Cut-Out Marilyn Maxwell"
**This page appeared in the February
23, 1948 issue of** *Life* **and also appeared in** *Good Housekeeping* **in March
1948.**

**"The Welcome That
Had To Be Washed Away"**
March 1928, *Junior Home*
**This was one of six different paper
dolls advertising Fels-Naptha soap. The
other five pages appeared in October,
November, December 1927 and January
and February 1928. They also
appeared in** *Child Life* **the same
months.**

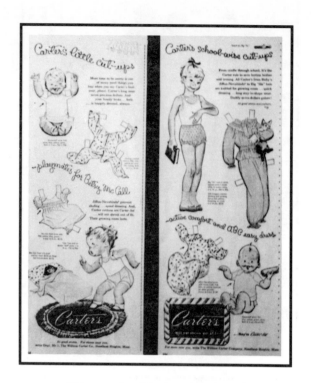

"Swan's Cut Out For 4 Big Jobs"
March 1944 was the date this ad
appeared in *Country Gentlemen* and
Ladies' Home Journal. It also appeared
in *Life* February 28, 1944 and possibly in other magazines.

"Carter's Little Cut-Ups"
March 1952

"Carter's School-Wise Cut-Ups"
September 1952

"Carter's Little Cut-Ups"
April 1952

"Carter's Gifted Cut-Ups"
November 1952

These Carter's ads by the William Carter
Company appeared in *McCall's* and possibly in
other magazines.

Price Guide

Paper dolls pictured are in mint condition and are priced as mint un-cut pages. Some photos are cropped for production purposes. A cut set, at most, would be worth half the price if complete.

Page 5 ....$6.00-10.00

The American Woman
Page 7 ....$8.00-12.00
Page 8 ....$8.00-12.00
Page 9 ....$8.00-12.00

American Family Journal
Page 10 ....$7.00-9.00

Butterick Fashion Magazine
Page 10 ....$7.00-9.00

Canadian Home Journal
Page 11 ....$10.00-14.00
Page 12 ....$10.00-14.00
Page 13 ....$8.00-12.00
Page 14 ....$8.00-12.00
Page 15
   August 1932 ....$8.00-12.00
   September & October 1932 ....$11.00-14.00
   November 1932 ....$8.00-12.00
Page 16 ....$8.00-12.00
Page 17
   April, May, June 1933 ....$8.00-12.00
   July 1933 ....$11.00-14.00
Page 18
   August, September,
    November 1933 ....$8.00-12.00
   March 1934 ....$11.00-14.00
Page 19 ....$8.00-12.00
Page 20 ....$8.00-12.00
Page 21
   May & June 1936 ....$8.00-12.00
   December 1936 ....$12.00-15.00
Page 22 ....$8.00-12.00
Page 23 ....$8.00-12.00
Page 24 ....$8.00-12.00

Children's Vogue
Page 24 ....$10.00-12.00

Comfort
Page 25 ....$4.00-7.00
Page 26 ....$4.00-7.00
Page 27 ....$4.00-7.00
Page 28 ....$4.00-7.00
Page 29 ....$4.00-7.00
Page 30 ....$4.00-7.00
Page 31 ....$4.00-7.00

The Delineator
Page 34 ....$12.00-16.00

Page 35 ....$12.00-16.00
Page 36 ....$12.00-16.00
Page 37 ....$12.00-16.00
Page 38 ....$12.00-16.00
Page 39 ....$12.00-16.00
Page 40
   September & October 1913 ....$12.00-16.00
   November 1913 ....$4.00-6.00
Page 41
   January 1914 ....$12.00-16.00
   February 1914 ....$4.00-6.00
   March & April 1917 ....$14.00-20.00
Page 42 ....$14.00-20.00
Page 43 ....$8.00-10.00
Page 44 ....$8.00-10.00
Page 45 ....$8.00-10.00
Page 46 ....$10.00-14.00
Page 47
   February, April & August 1921 ...$8.00-10.00
   January 1922 ....$3.00-6.00

The Designer
Page 48 ....$9.00-12.00
Page 49 ....$9.00-12.00

The Dolls' Dressmaker
Page 51 ....$9.00-12.00
Page 52 ....$9.00-12.00
Page 53 ....$9.00-12.00
Page 54 ....$9.00-12.00

Extension Magazine
Page 56 ....$7.00-9.00
Page 57 ....$7.00-9.00
Page 58 ....$7.00-9.00
Page 59 ....$7.00-9.00
Page 60 ....$7.00-9.00
Page 61 ....$7.00-9.00
Page 62 ....$7.00-9.00
Page 63 ....$7.00-9.00

The Farm Journal
Page 64
   November 1921 ....$6.00-8.00
   November 1924 ....$6.00-8.00
   October 1956 ....$2.00-3.00

The Farmer
Page 65 ....$5.00-7.00
Page 66
   April 1929/November 1928 ....$5.00-7.00
   August 1966 ....$3.00-6.00
   November 1964 ....$3.00-6.00

Page 67 .... $3.00-5.00

Good Housekeeping

Page 70 ....$12.00-15.00
Page 71
    October & November 1909 ....$12.00-15.00
    December 1911 ....$12.00-15.00
    April 1919 ....$6.00-8.00
Page 72 ....$10.00-15.00
Page 73 ....$10.00-15.00
Page 74 ....$10.00-15.00
Page 75 ....$10.00-15.00
Page 76 ....$10.00-15.00
Page 77 ....$10.00-15.00
Page 78 ....$10.00-15.00
Page 79
    August 1921 ....$10.00-15.00
    February 1922 ....$4.00-6.00
    October & November 1923 ....$9.00-12.00
Page 80 ....$9.00-12.00
Page 81 ....$9.00-12.00
Page 82 ....$9.00-12.00
Page 83 ....$9.00-12.00

The Grade Teacher

Page 84 ....$3.00-6.00
Page 85 ....$3.00-6.00

The Housekeeper

Page 87 ....$15.00-18.00
Page 88 ....$15.00-18.00
Page 89 ....$15.00-18.00
Page 90
    November 1910 ....$15.00-18.00
    January 1911 ....$15.00-18.00
    October 1911 ....$10.00-12.00
    December 1910 ....$7.00-9.00

Judge Magazine

Page 91 ....$10.00-12.00
Page 92 ....$7.00-9.00

Junior Instructor, Junior Home

Page 93 ....(for two page set) $7.00-10.00
Page 95 ....$7.00-9.00
Page 96 ....$7.00-9.00
Page 97 ....$7.00-9.00
Page 98 ....$7.00-9.00
Page 99 ....$7.00-9.00
Page 100 ....$7.00-9.00
Page 101 ....$7.00-9.00
Page 102 ....$7.00-9.00
Page 103
    April 1923 ....$4.00-7.00
    May 1923 ....$7.00-9.00
    October 1923 ....$7.00-9.00
    November 1923 ....$4.00-7.00
Page 104 ....$4.00-7.00
Page 105 ....$4.00-7.00

Page 106 ....$4.00-7.00
Page 107 ....$4.00-7.00
Page 108 ....$4.00-7.00
Page 109 ....$4.00-7.00

The Ladies' Home Journal

Page 113 ....$12.00-16.00
Page 114 ....$12.00-16.00
Page 115 ....$12.00-16.00
Page 116 ....$12.00-16.00
Page 117
    March, April & May 1910...........$12.00-16.00
    July 1910 ....$10.00-14.00
Page 118 ....$10.00-14.00
Page 119 ....$10.00-14.00
Page 120 ....$10.00-14.00
Page 121 ....$10.00-14.00
Page 122
    December 1911 ....$10.00-14.00
    July & October 1912 ....$9.00-12.00
    February 1913 ....$9.00-12.00
Page 123 ....$9.00-12.00
Page 124 ....$10.00-14.00
Page 125
    September 1915 ....$10.00-14.00
    November & December 1915 ....$8.00-10.00
Page 126 ....$10.00-14.00
Page 127 ....$10.00-14.00
Page 128 ....$10.00-14.00
Page 129 ....$10.00-14.00
Page 130 ....$10.00-14.00
Page 131 ....$10.00-14.00
Page 132 ....$10.00-14.00
Page 133
    September 1918 ....$10.00-14.00
    October, November &
      December 1918 ....$7.00-10.00
Page 134
    January 1919 ....$7.00-10.00
    September & November 1920 ......$7.00-10.00
    January 1922 ....$9.00-12.00
Page 135 ....$9.00-12.00
Page 136 ....$9.00-12.00
Page 137
    October, November &
      December 1922 ....$9.00-12.00
    January 1923 ....$8.00-10.00
Page 138 ....$8.00-10.00
Page 139 ....$8.00-10.00
Page 140
    October & November 1923 ....$8.00-10.00
    December 1923 ....$4.00-6.00
    September 1939 ....$4.00-6.00
Page 141 ....$3.00-5.00

Ladies' World

Page 142 ....$12.00-16.00
Page 143 ....$12.00-16.00
Page 144 ....$12.00-16.00

Page 145 .... $12.00-16.00

Life
Page 146 .... $9.00-12.00

McCalls
Betsy McCall (not pictured)
    1950's $4.00
    1960's $3.00
    1970's $2.00
    1980's $1.00
Page 153 .... $9.00-12.00
Page 154 .... $9.00-12.00
Page 155
    May & June 1911 .... $9.00-12.00
    August 1911 .... $6.00-8.00
    February 1914 .... $9.00-12.00
Page 156 .... $9.00-12.00
Page 157
    January 1916 .... $9.00-12.00
    March 1919 .... $4.00-6.00
    July & August 1919 .... $10.00-12.00
Page 158
    September 1919 .... $10.00-12.00
    October & November 1919 .... $9.00-12.00
    March 1920 .... $9.00-12.00
Page 159 .... $9.00-12.00
Page 160 .... $9.00-12.00
Page 161
    July 1921 .... $9.00-12.00
    August 1922 .... $5.00-8.00
    June 1925 .... $5.00-8.00
Page 162
    July & August 1925 .... $5.00-8.00
    September & October 1925 .... $9.00-12.00
Page 163 .... $9.00-12.00
Page 164 .... $9.00-12.00

McCall's Needlework
Page 164 .... $8.00-10.00

The Metropolitan
Page 165 .... $9.00-12.00
Page 166
    Vol. 29 #12, 1925/1926 &
      Vol. 30 #1, 1926 .... $9.00-12.00
    Vol. 30 #2, 1926 .... $5.00-7.00
Page 167 .... $5.00-7.00

Movie Magazine
Page 168 .... $18.00-24.00

Movies
Page 168 .... $14.00-18.00
Page 169 .... $14.00-18.00

Normal Instructor, Primary Plans, The Instructor
Page 170 .... $6.00-8.00

Page 171
    March 1911 .... $6.00-8.00
    June 1914 .... $6.00-8.00
    October 1920 .... $7.00-10.00
Page 172 .... $6.00-8.00
Page 173
    March 1932 .... $6.00-8.00
    November 1935 .... $5.00-7.00
    January 1937 .... $5.00-7.00
    December 1936 .... $5.00-7.00

Pageant
Page 174 .... (for the set) $35.00-48.00

Parents' Magazine
Page 175 .... $4.00-6.00

People's Popular Monthly
Page 176 .... $4.00-7.00
Page 177 .... $4.00-7.00
Page 178 .... $4.00-7.00

Pictorial Review
Page 182 .... $10.00-14.00
Page 183 .... $10.00-14.00
Page 184 .... $16.00-20.00
Page 185 .... $12.00-16.00
Page 186 .... $12.00-16.00
Page 187
    January 1916 .... $12.00-16.00
    March, April & May 1916 .... $14.00-18.00
Page 188 .... $14.00-18.00
Page 189 .... $14.00-18.00
Page 190 .... $14.00-16.00
Page 191 .... $14.00-16.00
Page 192 .... $14.00-16.00
Page 193 .... $14.00-16.00
Page 194 .... $14.00-16.00
Page 195 .... $14.00-16.00
Page 196 .... $12.00-15.00
Page 197 .... $12.00-15.00
Page 198 .... $12.00-15.00
Page 199 .... $12.00-15.00
Page 200 .... $12.00-15.00
Page 201 .... $12.00-15.00
Page 202 .... $12.00-15.00
Page 203 .... $12.00-15.00
Page 204 .... $12.00-15.00
Page 205 .... $12.00-15.00
Page 206 .... $12.00-15.00
Page 207 .... $12.00-15.00
Page 208 .... $12.00-15.00
Page 209 .... $12.00-15.00
Page 210 .... $12.00-15.00
Page 211 .... $12.00-15.00
Page 212 .... $12.00-15.00
Page 213 .... $12.00-15.00
Page 214 .... $12.00-15.00

Page 215
    December 1924 .... $12.00-15.00
    January & February 1925 .... $10.00-14.00
Page 216
    March 1925 .... $4.00-8.00
    May 1925 .... $10.00-14.00
    July 1925 .... $10.00-14.00
    January 1926 .... $8.00-12.00
Page 217 .... $8.00-12.00
Page 218 .... $10.00-14.00
Page 219 .... $10.00-14.00
Page 220 .... $10.00-14.00
Page 221 .... $10.00-14.00
Page 222 .... $10.00-14.00
Page 223 .... $10.00-14.00
Page 224 .... $10.00-14.00
Page 225 .... $10.00-14.00
Page 226 .... $10.00-14.00
Page 227 .... $10.00-14.00
Page 228 .... $10.00-14.00
Page 229 .... $10.00-14.00
Page 230 .... $10.00-14.00
Page 231 .... $10.00-14.00
Page 232 .... $10.00-14.00
Page 233 .... $10.00-14.00
Page 234 .... $10.00-14.00
Page 235 .... $10.00-14.00
Page 236 .... $8.00-10.00
Page 237 .... $8.00-10.00
Page 238 .... $8.00-10.00
Page 239 .... $8.00-10.00
Page 240 .... $8.00-10.00

The Prairie Farmer
Page 241 .... $3.00-6.00

Primary Education-Popular Educator
Page 241 .... $3.00-6.00
Page 242 .... $3.00-6.00

Screen Life
Page 243 .... $30.00-40.00
Page 244 .... $30.00-40.00

Simplicity Pattern Magazine
Page 245 .... $5.00-8.00
Page 246 .... $5.00-8.00

Today's Magazine
Page 247 .... $3.00-5.00

Vanity Fair
Page 248 .... $18.00-20.00

Page 249 .... $18.00-20.00

Woman's Day
Page 250 .... $3.00-5.00

Woman's Home Companion
Page 252 .... $20.00-30.00
Page 253 .... $20.00-30.00
Page 254 .... $20.00-30.00
Page 255 .... $20.00-30.00
Page 256
    December 1913 .... $20.00-30.00
    January & February 1914 .... $20.00-30.00
    March 1916 .... $3.00-6.00
Page 257
    March 1918 .... $6.00-10.00
    October 1919 .... $6.00-10.00
    April 1921 .... $6.00-10.00
    February 1920 .... $12.00-16.00
Page 258 .... $12.00-16.00
Page 259
    March & June 1921 .... $12.00-16.00
    November 1922 .... $10.00-14.00
    January 1923 .... $10.00-14.00
Page 260 .... $10.00-14.00
Page 261 .... $10.00-14.00
Page 262 .... $15.00-18.00
Page 263 .... $8.00-10.00
Page 264
    June 1927 .... $8.00-10.00
    October 1956 .... $2.00-3.00
    January 1942 .... $6.00-8.00

The Woman's Magazine
Page 265 .... $10.00-15.00
Page 266 .... $10.00-15.00
Page 267 .... $10.00-15.00
Page 268 .... $10.00-15.00
Page 269 .... $10.00-15.00
Page 270 .... $10.00-15.00
Page 271 .... $10.00-15.00

Advertising Paper Dolls
Page 271 .... $6.00-12.00
Page 272 .... $6.00-12.00
Page 273
    Life, April 1948 .... $6.00-12.00
    Life, February 1948/
    Good Housekeeping,
    March 1948 .... $6.00-12.00
    Jr. Home, March 1928 .... $5.00-8.00
Page 274
    Swan Ad, March 1944 .... $5.00-8.00
    March & November 1952 .... $3.00-5.00

Books on Antiques and Collectibles

Most of the following books are available from your local book seller or antique dealer, or on loan from your public library. If you are unable to locate certain titles in your area you may order by mail from COLLECTOR BOOKS, P.O. Box 3009, Paducah, KY 42002-3009. Add $2.00 for postage for the first book ordered and $.25 for each additional book. Include item number, title and price when ordering. Allow 14 to 21 days for delivery. All books are well illustrated and contain current values.

Books on Glass and Pottery

1810	American Art Glass, Shuman	$29.95
1517	American Belleek, Gaston	$19.95
2016	Bedroom & Bathroom Glassware of the Depression Years	$19.95
1312	Blue & White Stoneware, McNerney	$9.95
1959	Blue Willow, 2nd Ed., Gaston	$14.95
1627	Children's Glass Dishes, China & Furniture II, Lechler	$19.95
1892	Collecting Royal Haeger, Garmon	$19.95
2017	Collector's Ency. of Depression Glass, Florence, 9th Ed.	$19.95
1373	Collector's Ency of Amercian Dinnerware, Cunningham	$24.95
1812	Collector's Ency. of Fiesta, Huxford	$19.95
1439	Collector's Ency. of Flow Blue China, Gaston	$19.95
1961	Collector's Ency of Fry Glass, Fry Glass Society	$24.95
1813	Collector's Encyclopedia of Geisha Girl Porcelain, Litts	$19.95
1664	Collector's Ency. of Heisey Glass, Bredehoft	$24.95
1915	Collector's Ency. of Hall China, 2nd Ed., Whitmyer	$19.95
1358	Collector's Ency. of McCoy Pottery, Huxford	$19.95
1039	Collector's Ency. of Nippon Porcelain I, Van Patten	$19.95
1350	Collector's Ency. of Nippon Porcelain II, Van Patten	$19.95
1665	Collector's Ency. of Nippon Porcelain III, Van Patten	$24.95
1447	Collector's Ency. of Noritake, Van Patten	$19.95
1038	Collector's Ency. of Occupied Japan, 2nd Ed., Florence	$14.95
1719	Collector's Ency. of Occupied Japan III, Florence	$19.95
2019	Collector's Ency. of Occupied Japan IV, Florence	$14.95
1715	Collector's Ency. of R.S. Prussia II, Gaston	$24.95
1034	Collector's Ency. of Roseville Pottery, Huxford	$19.95
1035	Collector's Ency. of Roseville Pottery, 2nd Ed., Huxford	$19.95
1623	Coll. Guide to Country Stoneware & Pottery, Raycraft	$9.95
1523	Colors in Cambridge, National Cambridge Society	$19.95
1425	Cookie Jars, Westfall	$9.95
1843	Covered Animal Dishes, Grist	$14.95
1844	Elegant Glassware of the Depression Era, 3rd Ed., Florence	$19.95
2024	Kitchen Glassware of the Depression Years, 4th Florence	$19.95
1465	Haviland Collectibles & Art Objects, Gaston	$19.95
1917	Head Vases Id & Value Guide, Cole	$14.95
1392	Majolica Pottery, Katz-Marks	$9.95
1669	Majolica Pottery, 2nd Series, Katz-Marks	$9.95
1919	Pocket Guide to Depression Glass, 6th Ed., Florence	$9.95
1438	Oil Lamps II, Thuro	$19.95
1670	Red Wing Collectibles, DePasquale	$9.95
1440	Red Wing Stoneware, DePasquale	$9.95
1958	So. Potteries Blue Ridge Dinnerware, 3rd Ed., Newbound	$14.95
1889	Standard Carnival Glass, 2nd Ed., Edwards	$24.95
1941	Standard Carnival Glass Price Guide, Edwards	$7.95
1814	Wave Crest, Glass of C.F. Monroe, Cohen	$29.95
1848	Very Rare Glassware of the Depression Years, Florence	$24.95

Books on Dolls & Toys

1887	American Rag Dolls, Patino	$14.95
1749	Black Dolls, Gibbs	$14.95
1514	Character Toys & Collectibles 1st Series, Longest	$19.95
1750	Character Toys & Collectibles, 2nd Series, Longest	$19.95
2021	Collectible Male Action Figures, Manos	$14.95
1529	Collector's Ency. of Barbie Dolls, DeWein	$19.95
1066	Collector's Ency. of Half Dolls, Marion	$29.95
1891	French Dolls in Color, 3rd Series, Smith	$14.95
1631	German Dolls, Smith	$9.95
1635	Horsman Dolls, Gibbs	$19.95
1067	Madame Alexander Collector's Dolls, Smith	$19.95
2025	Madame Alexander Price Guide #15, Smith	$7.95
1995	Modern Collectors Dolls, Vol. I, Smith	$19.95

1516	Modern Collector's Dolls V, Smith	$19.95
1540	Modern Toys, 1930-1980, Baker	$19.95
2033	Patricia Smith Doll Values, Antique to Modern, 6th ed.,	$9.95
1886	Stern's Guide to Disney	$14.95
1513	Teddy Bears & Steiff Animals, Mandel	$9.95
1817	Teddy Bears & Steiff Animals, 2nd, Mandel	$19.95
2028	Toys, Antique & Collectible, Longest	$14.95
1630	Vogue, Ginny Dolls, Smith	$19.95
1648	World of Alexander-Kins, Smith	$19.95
1808	Wonder of Barbie, Manos	$9.95
1430	World of Barbie Dolls, Manos	$9.95

Other Collectibles

1457	American Oak Furniture, McNerney	$9.95
1846	Antique & Collectible Marbles, Grist, 2nd Ed.	$9.95
1712	Antique & Collectible Thimbles, Mathis	$19.95
1880	Antique Iron, McNerney	$9.95
1748	Antique Purses, Holiner	$19.95
1868	Antique Tools, Our American Heritage, McNerney	$9.95
2015	Archaic Indian Points & Knives, Edler	$14.95
1426	Arrowheads & Projectile Points, Hothem	$7.95
1278	Art Nouveau & Art Deco Jewelry, Baker	$9.95
1714	Black Collectibles, Gibbs	$19.95
1666	Book of Country, Raycraft	$19.95
1960	Book of Country Vol II, Raycraft	$19.95
1811	Book of Moxie, Potter	$29.95
1128	Bottle Pricing Guide, 3rd Ed., Cleveland	$7.95
1751	Christmas Collectibles, Whitmyer	$19.95
1752	Christmas Ornaments, Johnston	$19.95
1713	Collecting Barber Bottles, Holiner	$24.95
2018	Collector's Ency. of Graniteware, Greguire	$24.95
1634	Coll. Ency. of Salt & Pepper Shakers, Davern	$19.95
2020	Collector's Ency. of Salt & Pepper Shakers II, Davern	$19.95
1916	Collector's Guide to Art Deco, Gaston	$14.95
1753	Collector's Guide to Baseball Memorabilia, Raycraft	$14.95
1537	Collector's Guide to Country Baskets, Raycraft	$9.95
1437	Collector's Guide to Country Furniture, Raycraft	$9.95
1842	Collector's Guide to Country Furniture II, Raycraft	$14.95
1962	Collector's Guide to Decoys, Huxford	$14.95
1441	Collector's Guide to Post Cards, Wood	$9.95
1716	Fifty Years of Fashion Jewelry, Baker	$19.95
2022	Flea Market Trader, 6th Ed., Huxford	$9.95
1668	Flint Blades & Proj. Points of the No. Am. Indian, Tully	$24.95
1755	Furniture of the Depression Era, Swedberg	$19.95
1424	Hatpins & Hatpin Holders, Baker	$9.95
1964	Indian Axes & Related Stone Artifacts, Hothem	$14.95
2023	Keen Kutter Collectibles, 2nd Ed., Heuring	$14.95
1212	Marketplace Guide to Oak Furniture, Blundell	$17.95
1918	Modern Guns, Id. & Values, 7th Ed., Quertermous	$12.95
1181	100 Years of Collectible Jewelry, Baker	$9.95
1965	Pine Furniture, Our Am. Heritage, McNerney	$14.95
1124	Primitives, Our American Heritage, McNerney	$8.95
1759	Primitives, Our American Heritage, 2nd Series, McNerney	$14.95
2026	Railroad Collectibles, 4th Ed., Baker	$14.95
1632	Salt & Pepper Shakers, Guarnaccia	$9.95
1888	Salt & Pepper Shakers II, Guarnaccia	$14.95
1816	Silverplated Flatware, 3rd Ed., Hagan	$14.95
2027	Standard Baseball Card Pr. Gd., Florence	$9.95
1922	Standard Bottle Pr. Gd., Sellari	$14.95
1966	Standard Fine Art Value Guide, Huxford	$29.95
1890	The Old Book Value Guide	$19.95
1923	Wanted to Buy	$9.95
1885	Victorian Furniture, McNerney	$9.95

Schroeder's Antiques Price Guide

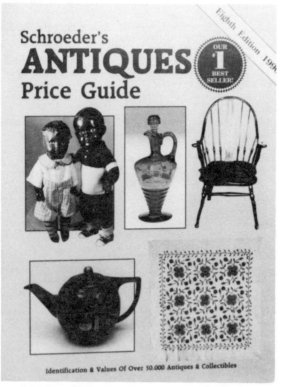

Schroeder's Antiques Price Guide has become THE household name in the antiques & collectibles industry. Our team of editors work year around with more than 200 contributors to bring you our #1 best-selling book on antiques & collectibles.

With more than 50,000 items identified & priced, *Schroeder's* is a must for the collector & dealer alike. If it merits the interest of today's collector, you'll find it in *Schroeder's.* Each subject is represented with histories and background information. In addition, hundreds of sharp original photos are used each year to illustrate not only the rare and unusual, but the everyday "fun-type" collectibles as well -- not postage stamp pictures, but large close-up shots that show important details clearly.

Our editors compile a new book each year. Never do we merely change prices. Accuracy is our primary aim. Prices are gathered over the entire year previous to publication, from ads and personal contacts. Then each category is thoroughly checked to spot inconsistencies, listings that may not be entirely reflective of actual market dealings, and lines too vague to be of merit. Only the best of the lot remains for publication. You'll find *Schroeder's Antiques Price Guide* the one to buy for factual information and quality.

No dealer, collector or investor can afford not to own this book. It is available from your favorite bookseller or antiques dealer at the low price of $12.95. If you are unable to find this price guide in your area, it's available from Collector Books, P.O. Box 3009, Paducah, KY 42001 at $12.95 plus $2.00 for postage and handling.

8½ x 11", 608 Pages   **$12.95**

COLLECTOR BOOKS

A Division of Schroeder Publishing Co., Inc.